UNCERTAIN JOURNEY

A woman's experience of living with cancer.

Anne Dennison

THE PATTEN PRESS

Newmill

1996

To Paul,

for the parts of this story that are written on water,

and to F.C.,

with love and thanks.

"Fate cannot be changed; or it would not be fate. Man, however, may well change himself, otherwise he would not be man."

Viktor Frankl

First published, 1996.

© The estate of Anne Dennison & The Patten Press, 1996

Cover illustration: Entrance to Otago Harbour, New Zealand, by Harry Miller, 1970. Reproduced by permission of his Estate.

Reprints of published articles by courtesy of the *British Medical Journal*, and *The Guardian*.

ISBN 1 872229 23 9

Designed & Typeset in-house at The Patten Press

Printed & bound by The Cromwell Press, Broughton Gifford, Melksham, Wiltshire

CONTENTS

Foreword

When on June 9 1989 Anne Dennison awoke from an anaesthetic she learned that far from the simple removal of an ovarian cyst she had expected, inoperable cancer had been discovered. At a single stroke at the age of thirty one lay shattered all her hopes -- for career, for children, for life itself. As she wrote in her diary -- she had been planting a garden she would never see and renovating a house for children she would never have.

Uncertain Journey shows that far from being the end of the story this event turned out to be a beginning. For during the remaining six years of her life she both came to terms with her own illness and in this book has left not only a poignant memorial but practical help for others. Her writings included not only some acerbic accounts of her frustrations with a well-intentioned but often sadly insensitive medical profession, but at a higher level a profound meditation on what for many of us will be an inevitable experience sooner or later. How to live in the face of the knowledge of approaching death. And this from a person of unflinching honesty who in referring to other books on cancer could write   'some of them seem to approach death with such calmness. I don't! Others conclude "I'm glad I had cancer". I'm not!'

In July 1988, Anne joined a civil service team set up to implement a radical reform of the British public health system and we became close colleagues. It was difficult to credit the news that she was at an advanced stage of a fatal illness. She discharged her role with such poise and efficiency; she had an easy friendly manner, and I do not remember seeing a shadow cross her face.

Concealed perhaps with an unconscious irony in the title Uncertain Journey there is for me one message in this book which is more important than all the others -- this is that certainty, even about death, is better than uncertainty and information better than ignorance. When Anne at last understood and accepted the significance of her illness much of her anger and frustration disappeared. Instead she found 'a new awareness -- intoxicating -- like being reborn' heightening her sense of beauty and deepening her relationships with her friends. Every day had to be made to count, every moment relished.

Anne found the decision to share her private diary and her reflections on it with others difficult. In the end she did so in the hope that her experiences and insights in coming to terms with potentially fatal cancer might assist not only doctors and nurses in dealing better with the sensitivities but also offer help to those who fear or suffer from this illness.

Such is the power of her message and the beauty of her prose that it is my belief that many thousands will indeed find help from this book.

Sir Donald Acheson, 1995

Sir Donald Acheson, KBE, MA, DM (Oxon), FRCP, FRCS, FRCOG, FFPHM, FFPHMI, FFOM

Department of Public Health & Policy, London School of Hygiene & Tropical Medicine, University of London.

INTRODUCTION

Deciding to let other people read this book is not easy. It is a very personal account. I started writing for myself alone. Explaining what had happened in the form of a narrative was no more than a useful device for ordering my thoughts. I simply wanted to sort out the bewildering and painful turmoil that began one sunny June morning four years ago when I was told I had advanced ovarian cancer. I was thirty one years old, happily getting on with my life, the uncertainties of my teens and early twenties finally over. Happy in my work and in my circle of family and friends. Suddenly, I felt, the axe had fallen. Gone forever.

Over the next few months I wavered between "Please God let it all be over soon I don't want the goodbyes to last forever" and "Please God I take that back, make it last as long as you can". I learnt that cancer wasn't an instant death sentence. I even began to imagine myself cured. I saw cancer as a temporary setback, not even a totally negative one. There was pain and loss, but on the other hand I had been given a chance to assess my life so far and make time for what was really important. Then, just as I was beginning to get used to the diagnosis, I found I was also incurable. It was unlikely that the cancer would ever go away. Unlikely; but even now I cannot bring myself to say impossible. You see that was nearly three years ago. I have a few problems from time to time but basically I'm very much alive and well.

I may have outlived my prognosis but I still have the disease. I think I should warn you now this book doesn't have a happy ever after ending. I cannot write a conventional "I conquered cancer" story. I read so many of them, looking for support from the only people I felt might really understand what I was going through; other patients. They seemed so sure of themselves. I envied them. They never seemed to feel they could cope one day and that they couldn't the next. They tried all the alternative remedies that I found so bewildering; rigorous diets, meditation, vitamins, herbal remedies. If they were sceptical they rarely said so. They didn't need to be. By the end of the book they were always free of cancer.

But what if the miracle doesn't happen? What if, like me, you are one of the many thousands of people who just have to learn to live with the disease. We have a much more restricted choice of autobiographies.

1

Some of them seem to approach death with such calmness. I don't. Others conclude "I'm glad I had cancer". I'm not.

So, to keep myself sane, I wrote about what I felt. Maybe someone who is still trying to make sense of it all will find it helpful to find another patient as mixed up as they feel.

When I am well and death is far away I can theoretically be grateful for the opportunities cancer has given me. I can live in new harmony with the past and have developed new strengths to go forward into the future. Then death comes closer and I find I'm not reconciled to the idea at all. The most I can say is that if I had the choice of dying tomorrow in an accident, never having had cancer, and dying tomorrow of my cancer, I'd choose to die of cancer. None of us wants to die but we all have to. We need a little time to get used to the idea. A few months, a few years, are precious. It can become a very positive experience. Not just for the patient. I think my family and friends have also benefitted.

Perhaps if more doctors could see the positive side they would find treating cancer patients a little easier. Too many still regard cure as the only mark of success. But it isn't. Lengthening the time after diagnosis is also important. Even that isn't enough. I'd like to see medicine take more of an interest in helping patients make the most of their lives. All patients, for even those who are "cured" cannot take it for granted. A little psychological support can make the difference between seeing cancer as a total disaster or an opportunity for new life. I was just lucky in finding the right books and the right people at the right time but others aren't so fortunate.

I hope then that this account of my experience might challenge those professionals who read it to think about ways they can help their patients regard a diagnosis of cancer as a beginning and not an end. Why should that be left to alternative practitioners who mix it up with bogus science? Maybe they will just find some insight into what the interesting carcinoma in bed sixteen is going through and learn to relate to patients on a more human level.

Maybe this book will also help people who don't have cancer but who fear it more than anything. They usually tell me how brave I am which means how scared they are. I want to share the discovery that still surprises me. Misery hasn't yet completely overwhelmed me. Bad as it is, pain never seems to last for long. I want to say "Yes it is painful but it is also endurable. It's not as frightening as you imagine."

Anne Dennison, April 1990

2

CHAPTER 1

THE DIAGNOSIS

What I remember most clearly about that night is the roses. Small, beautifully formed deep red roses. It was a joke really. When I had stayed in hospital overnight a few weeks before my husband Paul had brought me a bunch of daffodils. This time I was supposed to be in for four or five days to have an ovarian cyst removed. He asked me what flowers I would like. I laughed and said surely such a long stay was worth my favourite red roses. When I woke it was the first thing I saw. I managed to say "Hello love, it's nice to see you". I wanted to say more but it was such an effort. "The roses are lovely"...and then the fog descended. I remember feeling warm and heavy. The nurses fussed. That was odd. It didn't hurt nearly as much as the laparoscopy I had a few weeks ago, yet they definitely hovered, asking if I felt comfortable. I called them over twice to say I wanted to go to the toilet but they patiently told me both times that I had a catheter and not to worry.

Odd that. I had a drip in one arm just like the houseman had warned me but he had said there was only a slight chance of my coming back with a catheter or a drain. Well at least I didn't have the drain. Paul was there, that was the main thing. I didn't have the energy to ask what they had done, whether the biopsy had meant I had to have a whole ovary removed. And last night they had for the first time mentioned the possibility of malignancy. Only one in a hundred chance they said and I genuinely wasn't worried. Still, it was a possibility. I should find out but I felt so sleepy. I'm told I came in and out of consciousness several times, each time talking about the roses. That I only vaguely remember, though I can still see Paul holding my hand and smiling at me with a tear rolling down his nose. I remember thinking what a silly sentimental old thing he was before I fell asleep again. Then the next time I woke he was gone.

I really only came to the following morning. The usual round of temperatures and breakfast (not for me thank you). I wanted to ask what had been done. I could see the houseman further down the ward but I didn't want the houseman's version. Last time he had been unintentionally misleading. And patronising. I could understand the odd medical phrase and didn't want the simple censored version again.

I dozed off once more and Paul appeared. Pleasant surprise then sudden panicky dread. Something was wrong. He had a nurse with him; they were pulling the curtains round my bed. And he told me. No they hadn't just taken an ovary away. They'd taken it all. A complete hysterectomy. They'd discovered ovarian cancer. And they hadn't managed to remove it all, there was some cancer left.

3

Paul cried, I wished I could. I was appalled. I had never made him cry in all the years we had been together. I couldn't feel anything for myself. This couldn't be happening, not to ME.

There was only numbness and a strong physical sensation of having been kicked in the stomach. Everything gone all at once. This was some ridiculous black joke. It couldn't be happening. It was too much, too unexpected. My worst nightmare was infertility. That was bad enough but I hadn't even considered this. I just wasn't prepared. Too frightened I suppose to let myself think about it. God had really overdone it. Not only was I going to be childless, I had cancer. Not just early cancer either. What had I done to deserve it? I was bewildered more than anything. All those plans for the future. Meaning nothing. This couldn't be happening to me. I felt curiously detached. I heard the words. I can still see the concerned face of that nurse, but I couldn't really feel anything. Part of me couldn't believe it. But a still cold voice inside told me it was true.

We waited. In silence mostly. There wasn't much to say. The senior registrar was doing his rounds and I watched him gradually move down the ward. His feet stopped outside my curtains. He picked up my notes and stood there reading them over and over for a good ten minutes. Poor man, it can't have been easy. He had been responsible for me for the last couple of months, perplexed by my pain but reassuring they would find and treat the problem. We had always got on well. It can't have helped that my last words to him the night before were a half joking exhortation to take good care of my ovaries, that they were very precious to me. He had smiled, patted my hand and said "I know". All he could say on finally entering that morning was a bleak "I'm sorry". I rose as far out of the bed as tubes and drips allowed. "I just don't believe it" I said angrily, "it's only six weeks since the laparoscopy and there was no sign of this."

I wanted him to deny it, tell me it was all a mistake, but he could only nod blankly. I wanted to know everything. Now, at once. We discussed the size of the five tumours that had been removed, what was left, the proposed treatment. He tried to be reassuring - the size of the tumours left was very small, there were chances of an excellent response to chemotherapy. I wasn't at all reassured. He seemed unable to convince himself let alone me. There was a weariness in his voice and he didn't meet my eye. I knew nothing at all about cancer then but I could count and stage three didn't sound too hopeful. And chemotherapy! Continuous vomiting, hair going to fall out. I suddenly realised. I wasn't just maimed, I was going to be ill!

They left me then. I can't really describe the devastation I felt, it was mostly a blank nothingness. I remember too a strong sense of unreality. The comings and goings of the ward around me continued in the now familiar pattern. That added to my bewilderment; it was hard to

4

reconcile with the feeling that my own world had been utterly torn apart. I was going to die and for them it was just routine.

The drugs didn't help. The nurses continued to hover asking me if it hurt. My saying "Yes it does a bit" resulted in a jab that left me semi-conscious for the next four or five hours. After 24 hours I had had enough. "No it doesn't" I said. I was lying, it hurt like hell; but I wanted to think, to feel what was happening to me.

I was obsessed by the waste of it all. Thirty one years old, in the middle of a promising career, valued by family and friends. Now it was all going to end. All those years spent studying and establishing a career. Why had I bothered? What hope of my contributing now, just as my chances were opening up. All those days spent planting a garden I'd never see, renovating a house for a family that would never exist. Even I wasn't going to enjoy it for long. I regretted all the effort, all the sacrifices directed towards a future which wasn't going to happen. I was all such a waste, so pointless. There was a more banal side. I'd done some summer shopping before coming into hospital. I agonized about the waste of that too; an extravagant blouse and skirt I'd never wear. Big things and small, there was no priority. Pain has no sense of order.

Death? It just seemed so unreal. I'd never seriously considered the possibility that it could happen to ME. I had had a fortunate life. Death was something that happened to grandparents in their 70s and 80s. And the unfairness of it all. Why me? I knew it was ridiculous but all I could think over and over was that I'd never hurt anyone deliberately in my life. What had I done to deserve this? It was so unfair. If there was a God he couldn't do this, not to me. It wasn't FAIR.

This just couldn't happen. It didn't fit. I wasn't the kind of person disaster happened to. I was young and healthy. In control. I'd got pretty well what I wanted from life. At least I felt I had. Not wealthy but comfortable. After years of university life I was finally establishing a career in the big wide world. I had a supportive network of family and friends. I felt I had no more than anyone else I knew. I wasn't asking for fame and fortune just the comfortable educated middle class existence which everyone else I knew was enjoying. Why had I been singled out? Why was it going to end just for me? It wasn't fair. Why me? Why? Why? Why?

I couldn't believe something so significant could have happened to me without my knowing about it. I'd had some pain, I'd known something was wrong, but no one had given me any reason to suspect it was serious. My body had let me down, it wasn't reliable. Nothing could be trusted. Least of all myself.

I didn't really believe all those encouraging words. No one had promised treatment would definitely cure me. Cancer was an inevitable death sentence. Treatment was going to give me a bit more time but I was going to die. I was a little frightened. Maybe it could happen. It had grown so fast. If it really hadn't been there six weeks ago it might continue at the same rate. I could be dead within months.

The question that kept coming up again and again was: how long? No one would tell me, just waffle on about what an excellent chance chemotherapy had of curing me. I didn't know then that there never are any definite answers. I'd had the bad news, now I was ready for the full story. I wanted to know how long I had to round things off, to adjust, to come to terms with this shock. I needed time for practical things too, I hadn't seen my family in New Zealand for nearly three years.

Paul being there was the only thing which helped. We had no words of comfort for each other. We didn't really talk much at all, but his presence was enough. The nurses thought it rather odd I think to see him sitting at my bedside doing his end of year marking for hours on end. At least we were together now. Only he can describe the horror and loneliness of that first night when he knew and I didn't. I didn't want to see anyone else. Even my closest friends. Others had rung too asking if they could visit. I didn't want to face any of them just yet, or perhaps I didn't want them to see me in this paralysed state. I put them all off. I didn't want to talk to any of the other patients either who I think were rather hurt by my sudden withdrawal. I was too bewildered to talk to anyone. I just wanted to be alone. What I felt was too vague, too painful to be confined to words. I couldn't understand and accept what had happened myself and I didn't know how to communicate that to anyone except Paul.

Still raw with shock, I was very sensitive to the reactions of others. One houseman, bless him, continued to throw the odd Scots joke in my direction as he passed. The other, who had been responsible for me earlier, never came near me again. One nurse upset me tremendously. She seemed to be treating me quite as usual, then I caught her grimacing to a colleague "it's cancer". I felt like a freak, a leper. Her kindly concern felt like a patronising act.

The registrar continued to be as shocked as I was. He came to see me the following day and asked "How are you?". His mistake. I told him that I was still utterly devastated, that I couldn't really take it all in. He nodded, felt my stomach and said to the nurse that the drip and catheter could be removed. Then he was gone. His colleague patted my arm as he left. "We're all a bit shocked you know". I suddenly wanted to cry for the first time and I was angry too. I wanted to tell that registrar that my shock was the greater and the least he could do was show his some place else. I couldn't deal with my own emotions let alone spare the energy to deal with his.

I really wasn't interested in what anyone else was feeling. Even Paul at that stage. I was the one with advanced cancer. I was the one whose life had ended. I was the one going to be ill, maybe to die. But I didn't want to talk about it, and I didn't want to talk about how anyone else felt either.

Later that day a nurse came to whisper "the consultant's coming to see you tonight". The implication was this was a tremendous favour. I was unimpressed. I wanted to say "About time, she's responsible for this mess". Her visit was a turning point though. She had no more satisfactory explanation to offer as to why the disease had been missed earlier and I, deferential to doctors as usual, didn't challenge her to provide any. I was rather suspicious of her bland and optimistic reassurances about the possibility of a completely normal life. We needn't even be childless if we went for adoption. Huh. I would be in my late thirties before I could be certain of cure. Who did she think she was kidding?

What was important was her generally positive attitude, her repeated and emphatic insistence that I was young and fit and healthy. "Let's have a look at those stitches". I had a mental vision of my stomach springing open as she ripped off the plaster. Nothing but a thin bloody line and a few black stitches. "Looks fine." She gave me a calculating look. "How about going home tomorrow?" I jumped at the chance. Her attitude was infectious. Suddenly I was young and fit and healthy. My body had had one mechanical failure but it wasn't yet time to scrap the whole machine. I was still me.

There was something else too. It was not just that she reminded me of my strengths. She reminded me I was exactly the same person I had been three days earlier, not some strange new creature, a cancer victim. Sure, I had the surgery to recover from, but given the state of my general health that wasn't going to be a problem.

Her visit was a turning point. Later that evening I had the thought that if my life was to be limited it was plain stupid to lie there feeling sorry for myself. I could waste what time there was doing precisely that or I could make the most of each and every minute that was left. I often reminded myself of that moment. It was just a passing thought, trivial at the time, but it has become significant. I am still very aware that I have exactly the same choice now.

It was a long night. I didn't sleep, perhaps because I'd dozed so much in the past few days. There were no more blinding insights, just a mulling over of the same old "why me?" questions, but somehow I was becoming more aware of other people. I started to think of it from their perspective too. How would Paul survive without me? This was going to destroy two lives, not one. I tried to be positive. I'd rather deal with cancer myself than face the prospect of living life without Paul. He must be going through hell too. I wanted to get out of hospital and really talk to him.

The next morning word had got around that I was going home. The junior doctors were aghast. "You can't go home at three days". "Dr X

7

said she could". "Oh". Then they tried to bribe me. "But we were going to get the oncologist to see you". No dice. I'd see her next week in outpatients anyway. "But all the tests we've got to do". Well I had a busy morning. By lunchtime I too was beginning to wonder if it was a good idea. My strength was wearing out and I couldn't face getting dressed. So I walked to the car in my dressing gown. Those corridors have never felt so long.

The ward had begun to feel less alien anyway. The gossips had been at work and I was at last able to say to the other patients that I had cancer. I needn't have worried about their reaction. "So have I love" said Grace in the next bed. Daphne in the bed opposite turned out to have it too. I confessed I was worried about the treatment they were proposing. "Oh it's not too bad, I've had two lots of chemotherapy and I'm still here. When you really need to worry is when they tell you they've got no more treatment to offer you". (She was so right!) But I wanted to go. I needed to get out of hospital. I couldn't deny I had cancer, but I could deny it was going to make me ill. I had had enough for the time being.

It was time to look forward. Without ever talking about it Paul had understood. When he came to collect me from hospital he gave me a beautifully engraved locket he had bought in the antique market that morning. It was a token, his way of saying he knew what I had been thinking but I was wrong. He expected me to be around for a long time to come. It was a perfect gesture, even though writing it down makes it seem banal and sentimental. I needed his declaration of faith, it was more than medicine could give me.

CHAPTER 2

THE FIRST WEEKS

Home again. The garden, the hallway, upstairs to my own bed. It was sunny and warm, light streaming in the bedroom window. Nothing had changed, not really.

Now I was home I had to face the outside world though. Not all at once, one step at a time. But I had to do it now, while I had the energy, still on a bit of a high having got out of hospital. My parents in New Zealand were first. At least I didn't have to break the news to them. I had given Paul that unhappy task. I couldn't face them myself. I couldn't do it. I just couldn't. Again and again Paul had had to break the news to friends and family. It was just the initial telling. I couldn't bear to hurt them so deeply.

I rang New Zealand to say I was home, feeling O.K. if a bit tired, and I was going to fight with all my strength. And their flowers were wonderful. They were a bit overwhelmed but so encouraged that "I sounded so like myself." Many of my callers over the next few weeks said that. How could I not sound like myself? What were they expecting, some kind of pathetic invalid voice? Well I was beginning to feel like a pathetic invalid, so to bed.

We were in the midst of a heatwave; the next day I enjoyed the sun in a deckchair round the side of the house, away from the eyes of neighbours. I did not yet feel like casual conversation. I was so glad to be convalescing at home in the sun rather than in hospital. The following day I was up to my first visitors, my two oldest and dearest friends. I guess we were all a little apprehensive at the meeting, but in the end we just hugged each other. They were as glad to see me as I was to see them. With them too I expressed my determination to fight. This was something I genuinely believed, a response to the exhilaration at escaping from hospital, but in the early days there was also an element that was less a matter of my personal commitment than a need to support my family and close friends. I had hurt and shocked them so much by getting this disease, in some way I was trying to make amends by being determined to fight it.

In retrospect it is difficult to describe the luminous intensity of those first few days at home. It was very hot, and I spent most of the time dozing in the garden. I was blissfully conscious of beauty, warmth, the sheer sensuous pleasure of convalescence. Lying in the sun in my garden for days on end was not something I had had time to do before. And of course the closeness between Paul and me was much heightened and very tender. I remember looks, gestures, moments. They seemed to sum up and contain the essence of all that had ever been between us. I didn't have any answers to the why me? questions. I didn't have the energy to be angry. It just seemed to be a matter of pathos, not great tragedy now.

I wondered whether the shock had made me mad. I felt so alive, so happy and so selfconscious. I was deeply aware of how much I enjoyed my life. Sometimes it was intoxicating, like being reborn with a new awareness. Everyday sensations, the sun on my arms, listening to a favourite piece of music, were more intense than they had ever been before. Specific moments which now seem so trivial seemed so significant at the time. I was happy NOW. I didn't want time ever to move. I just wanted to keep the moment. I convinced myself that eternity wasn't forever it was a quality of life. And I had it now. The future was irrelevant.

That heightened sensitivity was the other side of despair. I was aware for the first time how fragile life was. I might lose all this. It really was happening. I had cancer. I might die. Fear was making me appreciate life consciously for the first time. Only very rarely did panic take over. When it did I reminded myself of that last night in hospital and that I still had the same choice as to whether or not I wasted whatever time was left. By and large willpower won in the early days. I would not give in.

I was still bewildered though. I started to keep a diary. It begins:

I feel conscious of the need to begin writing this tonight. One week ago exactly about this time they must have been cutting it all out. How many times since have I thought if only I could put the clock back. The first of the "If onlys". I need to write. I've never kept a diary before but I need to sort out what I think. I say so much. So many things I think I feel. I wonder sometimes what it is I feel. Right now I wonder whether I feel anything at all. Perhaps it's all just words.

There was too a continuing fierce determination not to give into pain, perhaps a reaction to the hurt of the previous week. The diary quickly became a series of erratic notes. On rereading it seems I was trying to convince myself as much as anyone :

I'm recovering from the operation but I don't feel any different on a day to day basis... I can take each day as it comes and make the most of it... We've always said it would be nice to spend more time in each other's company at this time of year when Paul has so much free time...

That kind of intensity can't be sustained for long. My return to reality came with my return to hospital. I had been in and out a couple of times for various tests, but the change came with my outpatients appointment a week after discharge; to have my stitches removed, discuss the pathology report and meet the radiotherapist who would be in charge of me from now on, starting with my first chemotherapy treatment the following day. I was reluctant to go, to break the spell of the week we had just had. Maybe if I didn't do anything it would all go away.

Gynae outpatients was as crowded as usual, but this time I didn't wait for long. All those symptoms now had a label. Cancer. A very significant label. No more vague implications that I was making a fuss about nothing. Yet I hadn't changed, nor had my condition, but now I was the centre of attention and Paul and I were whisked in to see my consultant. Practical details were soon over: "stitch cutter please nurse". Then the important bit. The pathologist's report. I had been told this would answer the question of how malignant the tumours were, whether the cancer was poorly or highly differentiated. I had prayed fervently that it would be of low malignancy, I felt God at least owed me that. It couldn't be bad news, after all I felt so well. I would have known. I got my first set back. "Moderately differentiated". It really was true. I did have cancer. Somewhere at the back of my mind was still the hope that it was all a dreadful mistake.

The odds weren't stacked against me completely. By the end of the day I was writing in my diary that "it reinforces that neutral feeling. I feel in some way it's up to me to kick it to the positive side of the line". The radiotherapist had told me there was a 50/50 chance that the chemotherapy would eradicate the disease. I grinned at Paul's glumness and reminded him that I'd never been anywhere near the bottom 50% for anything in my life, but I was a little shocked too. This was something completely new in my experience. A medicine whose results could not be guaranteed. Deep down I'm not sure I really believed bad things really happened even then.

The radiotherapist was brisk and cheerful. A little too cheerful for my liking. This was a serious matter after all. I could take it with a joke, but I expected doctors to have more respect. More disturbing at that first appointment was my inability to get any serious conversation going about why, how and where we were going. The radiotherapist answered the questions that I thought of in the few minutes she was present for the introduction. We discussed the chances of success and side effects. I could expect some nausea but no hair loss. What a relief that was. On the spur of the moment I didn't think to ask about alternatives. Then she was gone.

Everything was going so fast. I didn't know how to ask whether perhaps it might be better to go elsewhere for treatment. This was a London teaching hospital. Surely they were much the same? What about a bigger more specialist unit? Would they be able to offer me more? I had noticed from the banners outside that the hospital was raising money for a CT scanner. Did that mean they didn't have the latest equipment? What would be the point in going elsewhere? Surely there was just one standard treatment? (Little did I know then!) I didn't know how to stop the momentum. Everyone just assumed I would stay where I was and I didn't want to make a fuss. It would look as if I was questioning their competence.

I wanted to talk about the disease too. A lot of my shock in those early days was about having ovarian cancer. I worked for the Department of Health; I prided myself on a good general knowledge of at least women's health matters. My impressions of ovarian cancer had been that it was a rare condition that affected little old ladies. I had heard of ovarian tumours, seen pictures of large benign cysts, and when I was told that they wanted to take mine out because "it will continue to grow and cause you trouble" I had assumed that was what they meant. But I digress.

I knew there were no definitive answers to the question why it had affected me, but there had to be some information, some general explanation about why cancer grew and why ovarian cancer in particular grew which would make what happened seem less like a completely random thunderbolt.

After going through the pathologist's report in some detail, the gynaecologist told me she had other patients to see and suggested I talk to the radiotherapist. She, unfortunately, was now too busy to see me, I was told by a nurse when I arrived. "Don't fuss, you'll see her on the ward tomorrow", she said. But I wanted information now. The gynaecologist had said, when I asked how I could find out more about this disease, "well you're capable of reading the textbooks". All well and good, but they weren't exactly accessible on the shelves of the libraries and bookshops of suburban South London. I was desperate. I demanded Paul stop at the local bookshop on the way home.

I wanted to know more about cancer, and I also knew a lot had been written recently about alternative therapies. If conventional medicine had so few guarantees I'd better get as much help as I could from other sources. I had heard of the Bristol Cancer Help Centre and knew there were lots of books about that might be useful. Friends from work had already given me the names of a few organisations who could supply medical and practical information, but it was only after going back to the hospital I felt like following them up. I was having to face the fact I couldn't stand still any more. The cancer wasn't going to go away while I ignored it. Time to move on. Finding a book about the so-called "alternative" therapies for cancer was the constructive outcome of the trip.

I also found a short text giving a brief resume of the prognosis for various kinds of cancer. Stage 3 ovarian cancer - about a 7% chance of 5 year survival. Another jolt to the stomach. My suspicions had been right. Oh God. It also stated that ovarian cancer was a disease that initially responded well to chemotherapy but often came back and didn't respond again. So much for all those bland reassurances.

Maybe I shouldn't have opened that book? I had to know. I had suspected anyway. I suddenly felt very much the fragile post operative patient. My knees started to wobble as I walked to the car. It was a sunny morning. The street was full of busy mothers purposefully shopping while their children were at school. It was all so normal. And so unreal. I wasn't one of them any more. Nothing would ever be the same again. I was only going to live a few years if I was lucky.

I was quiet that afternoon. I remember reading about the Bristol Centre and it's methods with a certain desperation. Surely some of the therapies which other people had found helpful might help me? It was, and is still, by no means an easy process. My immediate reaction was bewilderment and some horror. This was no gentle way. The book I was reading described methods which seemed more daunting than chemotherapy: coffee enemas, a completely raw food diet, weird "alternative" remedies based on apricot kernels, massive doses of vitamins. I find my reaction something to laugh at now, but I was more ambivalent at the time. I went through agonies of indecision but I decided I really couldn't face a rigorous diet. Was I missing out on the only real chance I had? I was daunted by the time and energy that would be required. I was only an erratically interested cook at the best of times, with no manufactured or preserved foods allowed I could see the few precious days I had left spent searching for and preparing organic carrots!

In the end I made some moves towards a more vegetarian and wholefood diet, but this was no more than a slight acceleration of changes I had started to make years ago. We already ate little red meat, now I began to experiment with the odd vegetarian dish. Not too much to begin with, I decided I needed good quality animal protein to recover from the surgery. As the months went by I became a better vegetarian cook, though some compromises were necessary. My closest friends are not vegetarian and I had no wish to break our tradition of a long and leisurely conversational lunch or dinner with a few good bottles of wine and a substantial meat course followed by a rich dessert. Such occasions were a much needed pleasure, a reminder that important things hadn't changed. Sometimes I just wanted to concentrate on what was the same as before, not the differences my illness had brought. Paul continued to stipulate for many months that if it was vegetarian he would have a chop with his thank you.

I was immediately taken with another aspect of the alternative therapies however; their common insistence that patients could help themselves by cultivating a positive attitude. Visualisation and meditation sounded interesting as well. So what did I have to lose? I had already done some relaxation exercises at a yoga class and I remembered them as helpful. I was out in the garden, I think the first attempt was more dozing than meditating but it was a start.

Then reality intruded. I had to go to hospital the next day for my first ever chemotherapy session. It would be done on an outpatient basis in future, but for the first dose they wanted me in hospital overnight. I bounced in full of meditation induced optimism. It was shortlived. There is no cancer ward at the hospital where I am treated, just a few beds on an acute medical ward mainly occupied by elderly diabetics. Or as I wrote in my diary at the time: "it's more about sick people I guess. Up in (the surgical gynae ward) it was really pretty optimistic. We were all, for the most part, well. Often having a pretty gruesome time in the short term but basically well and looking forward to going home after our operations".

I was for the first time introduced to the Great British Public's reaction to cancer. I had no inhibitions now about telling people what was wrong with me when they asked. I was ill-prepared for the response of the middle aged man sitting opposite me at dinner. His face crumpled. "Oh God, oh how terrible, oh I am sorry". I needed all my resources of cheerful optimism to reassure him it wasn't too bad, that I wasn't in any pain and a few months of chemotherapy had a good chance of beating it.

I wasn't really as cool as I tried to appear. I was seething with unanswered questions. I lay there waiting for my doctor and filled in time by writing in my diary. "I have so many questions - why and how and what might happen. Do I really want to know the last? But I need to know so much." I had already told the first doctor I met that I had many questions to ask the consultant. "You can ask me" he had said peremptorily. So I asked a few of those that sprung to mind. "Did ovarian cancer come back after treatment." "Yes sometimes." "What would happen then." "We'd look at that when we came to it." "Did it spread elsewhere in the body?" "Yes sometimes." Silence. "Any more questions?" Well there were thousands but this didn't seem the ideal way to have them answered. I said no.

I continued to wait for my consultant. She bustled in just as I was having dinner. She examined me quickly and said "You're some kind of teacher aren't you?" "No". I was puzzled. "But my husband's a lecturer. I'm a civil servant." "Oh. Well they'll be wondering when you're fit to go back I expect. I'd say after your next chemotherapy." I didn't know how to explain. I had loved not just my job but the career that went with it. Now it all seemed irrelevant and so very far away. I didn't give a damn right then. The gynaecologist too had talked a lot about how important it was to go back to work. They all seemed to expect me to just pick myself up and carry on as if nothing had happened.

I was hungry, tired of waiting and very apprehensive about the che-motherapy. All those questions I had been saving up didn't immediately come and then she was gone. They would now have to wait till outpatients in three weeks time.

I was drugged to minimise the effects and that first time I wasn't too sick. Home again the next day, and a renewal of the desperate attempts to be positive.

I keep telling myself this time last week I could hardly move. I had to get Paul to push me out of a chair my diaphragm was so sore. Just one week ago. Now I can move O.K. I'm just so tired all the time. I keep telling myself; a good sign of convalescence. Positive thinking must be important. I do try and meditate once or twice a day; sometimes I wonder whether I relax deeply enough. I'm trying to help the chemotherapy to do it's work. It seems silly and superstitious to write it down but I do have a strong mental image of golden hands clearing up the black crumbs of the remaining cancer. Sounds fanciful but I see it so clearly. Everything is in a neutral phase. I must turn it to the positive. There's a passive streak in me that says tough, your time has come, but I must not give in to it. A normal but childless life. That I could live with.

The reality of treatment did temporarily break the spell of the holiday, the reprieve we had just had. I wrote:

Paul has withdrawn today, been moody, depressed. I wish he had a close friend, was able to talk to someone as I can inflict my innermost thoughts on anyone who cares to listen. I feel I can't really help, I'm too close. After all it's me he's worried about. We'll see it through. Regain that closeness we had last week. It's just like it ever is, closeness comes and goes.

The first session of chemotherapy reinforced my horror of being ill, of being a tame patient. An understandable distrust of doctors and a knowledge there was no certainty they could help me left me determined to do as much as I could to help myself. I had always felt better for being physically fit. Why should I stop now? The physical training programme began. Even before going back to hospital I had managed a couple of walks around the local park, albeit with lots of stops. Four days after chemotherapy it was once around Hampstead Heath with a friend who complained "this isn't a walk, it's a route march." By the weekend it was a favourite five mile country walk. That was overdoing it rather, the next day was spent back in my garden deckchair, dozing. I hadn't been given any guidance about how to get myself fit after a hysterectomy, but I instinctively felt I should be a bit careful of my stomach. I soon proved there was nothing wrong with my legs though. I was able to start playing tennis again a few weeks later. Swimming, long a favourite form of exercise and relaxation, took a little longer as even lying on my front was painful at first, but I was back in the pool well within a couple of months of surgery. Enjoyable exercise, which is for me swimming, incompetent games of tennis and squash and long country walks, continues to be very important to me and kept me sane through the long months of chemotherapy.

But I am getting ahead of myself. The next couple of weeks were a happy mix of enjoying my returning strength and raiding bookshops for further inspiration. I discovered and devoured the Simonton's book on "Getting Well Again". It was so hopeful, so sure that a cancer patient's own psychology could if not cure at least help them to live longer. The book also set out a detailed programme of exactly what a patient could do to help herself. I was less convinced about the idea that psychology had any role in causing the disease though. The analysis of the cancer personality worried me; I refused and refuse to acknowledge that I felt helpless and hopeless, or unduly stressed, in the months before diagnosis. I had had my emotional ups and downs, (who hasn't) but nothing out of the ordinary. But it worried me. Perhaps it was so deeply buried in my subconscious I was unable to recognise it and unable to recognise it was still doing me harm?

The practical suggestions for coping, turning to the positive, I accepted immediately. They conceptualised and expanded what I had instinctively felt. There were other books too. Many of the most daunting kind. They were all on the theme I cured myself of cancer. It was only the methods which varied; rejecting orthodox medicine, meditating three times a day, eating nothing but beansprouts or wheatgrass. (Still, if they did it maybe I should try....) There were a few which helped, a few which didn't ask too much of a patient rather lacking in energy. They emphasised the healing potential of willpower and lighthearted distraction. That I could identify with. I had also found a couple of helpful general texts on cancer. Although they had nothing on ovarian cancer they explained so much my doctors had glossed over, such as terms like cell differentiation, that for the first time I began to understand what was going on.

This is beginning to sound like one of those inspirational tales I was anxious to avoid, but there was genuinely little depression or negative feelings of any kind in those early weeks. The shock of the diagnosis was so great that it produced a grim determination not to allow it to be repeated. The nearest I can get to a response of this sort is a diary entry made a few days after the first chemotherapy session.

Wednesday I went to see (my GP). Awkward. He didn't connect me with the form he had got from the hospital. I had to tell him they found out what was wrong with me at last. My voice faltered a bit. First time I had to break the news face to face. Still he was good. Nothing new to say but he made me talk. It helped to talk to someone not involved with me. No need to buoy him up. He asked was I angry - he would be. I thought that through. I'm not angry at tragedy. It's too big for that. Anger seems too ridiculous. Too petty. Angry at stupidity, waste and mismanagement. Angry at the chain of disasters in my case, the delays, the missing it all that time... But these are the "if onlys". I will not dwell on them. I can't change them, if I dwell on them I will go under. I think I'm getting used to it. There are bad days, minutes really. Flickers of resentment at other people's happiness. John (my brother) wrote to me on Friday. I feel so envious of his happiness, planning his wedding to a girl my age. I wish him no harm, but why me and not him?

16

That seems to have been almost the only sign that all was not well in the best of all possible worlds. I was being positive about everything. From the opportunities I presented by the warm weather for the longest, laziest holiday I'd had in years to the benefits of childlessness. "I'll make the most of it God, just give me the chance."

In retrospect I wonder whether I have got that quite right. I do remember lying in bed a few days after chemotherapy, unable to concentrate on a novel. There simply seemed no point in literary interests any more. But it was only a momentary weakness I allowed myself. I concentrated on what was positive. Family and friends and fine summer days. My world extended no further than my front door.

CHAPTER 3

REALITY SETS IN.

I had to let go a little eventually though. Again the catalyst was a trip to hospital. Again my diary records my feelings most immediately:

Breezed in for the three week check up and found a reception from the radiotherapist and the gynaecologist was just as breezy. Nothing was particularly abrupt, I was just feeling vulnerable, my first time near a hospital for three weeks. And having an audience of three, they had a junior doctor in there as well, was offputting. Has it's funny side too I suppose, me looking down to see three faces peering up the speculum! But distressing too. The radiotherapist was a bit rough and then said "Better use a lubricant with intercourse, you don't exactly relish vaginal examinations." Who does? Then she gave me a rectal examination. No warning whatsoever and wondered why I jumped six inches off the bed. The gynaecologist was very gentle but no more assertive. Simply saying to the radiotherapist what about hormones "She has an implant", what about sex "use a lubricant", but seemed powerless to take control and talk about these things himself. The upshot was I came away in a very disturbed state.

That night I couldn't sleep, in fact I had a couple of rough days. The check up had brought it all back and I kept reliving all those scenes where they told me, the check, everything, like a flood I couldn't stop. The hysterectomy, the never being able to have a child hit me hard too. It seemed that all I had been defiantly and determinedly putting out of my mind hit me at once. The reaction from work hasn't helped much either. All those collections. The cards and flowers were nice, even the first $20 I could happily spend on new tapes for my little stereo, but now another $50 "for flowers". I still haven't decided whether or not to give it to charity. I don't want anyone to feel I'm rejecting their kindness but on the other hand I don't want them to regard me as a lost cause."

This turmoil lasted the few days to my next chemotherapy which produced what became the usual reaction, prolonged vomiting uncontrolled by anti-sickness drugs. Perhaps the first dose had just been a light one to test my reactions. I was taken into hospital for rehydration after 15 hours of non-stop vomiting. I wrote of that stay:

Made me feel so vulnerable, so out of control. Partly the depression was due to feeling so ill. I realise that feeling well is an essential part of my rejection of the possibility that the cancer could get the better of me. When I don't feel well that possibility overwhelms me. Still as Paul says, if I feel ill think of what the cancer cells must feel.

Although this was no once and for all turning point, it is true to say that from that time on downs and ups were in a more realistic balance. Depression never seemed to last though. The following day I wrote:

Human again. The sickness is wearing off and it all seems like a bad dream. I'm feeling rather tired and washed out but alive again. We've just been for a walk round Dulwich park stopping at the pub on the way home. It's a lovely summer evening...

Still, I was now able to allow myself to relax and be depressed once in a while. Occasionally I could whisper to Paul "I'm scared, I don't know what's going to happen" or "Why? It's so unfair, I never did anything to deserve this." There were no answers; we would just curl up together and listen to music or watch rubbish on the television.

The circle was widening. It was time to make contact with the outside world. My doctor had predicted I would be fit to go back to work six weeks after surgery, but when the time came I found I didn't feel like it. I had no stamina. I would be myself for a few hours but then feel overwhelmingly weary. I found a book which suggested the usual convalescence was nearer ten to twelve weeks so I decided I was justified in taking things a little more gradually. I was beginning to relish the time I had with Paul while he was on holiday from college and I needed a little time for psychological as well as physical recovery. I went into work for a couple of days though, to get the initial meetings over with and to find out how the Department had coped without me.

Work had always been a big part of my life. The day before the operation I was more concerned about what would be the outcome of a report I had been working on and what I would be missing over the next fortnight than whether or not that troublesome cyst was malignant. Then, overnight, that whole world became completely irrelevant. Now I was changing again. I was becoming a little bored with my restricted horizons.

I found going back a fairly exhausting process. I had from the beginning refused to be evasive about my disease. In the early days this was easy. When friends rang to say "I heard about your ...er ...illness", I replied "Have you heard the full story?" which I then told them in some detail making sure the word cancer featured easily and often. All my friends at work wanted a "quiet chat". Describing what had happened, sharing my hopes and fears over and over, was pretty hard work after such a long absence. I still felt being open was preferable to being the subject of covert gossip, but there were days when I wondered whether I had done the right thing. The curiosity wasn't always easy to take. Sometimes I was very self-consciously aware of the stares of those who did not know me well enough to say anything face to face. I was amazed at the speed with which the news seemed to have got around the entire Department. There was no respite.

19

Then there were others to chase. Those who had sent cards, again saying how sorry they were I was "ill". Good friends, and some brave others, telephoned, but by this stage it was obvious I would have to take some initiative with the rest. So I rang them to thank them for their cards, and again and again explained the "full story". It helped. Once the ice was broken the contacts were maintained and it says a great deal for my friends that I cannot think of any who shrank from that openness. In fact most have commented how much they appreciated it.

Being open was difficult enough where the diagnosis was already known. What I found hardest was having to break the news to totally unprepared friends and colleagues, those who just hadn't seen me for a couple of months but had no reason to suppose I wasn't as healthy as I always looked. I was by now quite comfortable in talking casually about having cancer, but unprepared recipients of the news were unable to hide their distress. That in turn distressed me. I learned to avoid the subject if I was unsure whether my listener knew.

It had it's funny side I suppose. How do you break the news gently to someone who says "I haven't seen you around for ages. Where have you been?" "Er, I've not been very well." "Oh no, not another of our bright young things for maternity leave." "Er, no." (And now my girl, if openness it's going to be...) Or "Oh dear, things all getting a bit much were they?" (Women aren't really up to this job.) "No, nothing like that, it's a bit more serious." "Well you can tell me I'm a doctor." I told him; that particular colleague still gives me a cheery wave as he passes but no longer stops to chat.

It is hard for many people to use the word cancer as an unemotional description of an illness. I remember vividly a rather funny conversation with a six year old friend. We were travelling together in the back of a crowded London bus on a Saturday afternoon. She was at the "Why?" stage. First we talked about why buses had bigger wheels than cars. A short silence. The bus moved and everyone else fell silent. Then a small voice piped up "Why did you get cancer Anne?" To her it was just another question, but the rest of the bus froze. I was angry at the stares of the other passengers. They were making me embarrassed and I wanted to be able to explain as innocently as she had asked.

I can't say I've experienced people avoiding me entirely, as so many cancer patients report, but there certainly are awkwardnesses. Many people don't ask me "How are you?" any more. I'm more likely to get a hearty "You look well." No one gets off that easily! Openness means that I will not let anyone else deny reality either. My response is usually a laughing "I am well, perfectly well. Not cured but well." If my openness is going to do anything may it convince a few more people that cancer is not an instant death sentence. Nor is it something to be denied, but an illness that can be lived with like any other. Sometimes that "You look well" is a bit more questioning. Then I add a progress report on the state of my health since they last saw me. You can sense their relief that they've got the information they wanted without feeling they asked the wrong question at the wrong time to get it.

A diagnosis of cancer seems to change everyone affected. Some people have reacted by becoming closer, expressing as never before their feeling for me. Others have become more distant as if they are anticipating separation in advance; some people seem to go through phases of both! Bot no one stays the same.

I changed too. Because it was rather a tiring business sharing my thoughts and emotions, I tended to spend more time with my closest friends while I had less time than before for others. This brought it's own rewards. I had a circle of good friends among my work colleagues. We had supported each other through what we had thought were the odd "crises" but none of us had had any major traumas. The sharing of my thoughts about what has happened and is happening has created an intimacy which (I hope!) both parties value. In turn they now share their problems with me much more freely. The same process has happened even more powerfully with my very closest friends. In addition, they have said they feel they have benefitted from the reminder of their own mortality and their need to sort out life's priorities. They too perceive that the future is uncertain, so the important thing is to make the most of the opportunities given today. One friend recently complained that as a consequence it was my fault she was now always broke!

But I am in danger of trivialising a process which was as painful and as complex for them as it was for me. And I am getting ahead of myself again.

I was only really beginning to deal with the world, slowly and hesitantly. It was one thing to enjoy each and every day lazing in the sun with Paul and my friends. Quite another to keep the same perspective in the hurly burly of work and "real" life. So I took it slowly. A few days at work, then back for a few days off. A few more days back at work to discuss what I would do when I returned, then a holiday.

A normal holiday. We went to Austria, the only concession to my weakened state was that it was a package deal, two weeks in the same hotel, not touring and camping as usual. I had thought about going to a residential cancer help centre but in the end decided the money would be better spent on a good holiday. I didn't particularly want to concentrate on having cancer any more. It seemed more important to get as far away as possible from sickness and hospitals in the weeks between chemotherapy.

Austria was as fun and as busy as our holidays always are; climbing mountains day after day, exploring Salzburg, getting inveigled into crossing a glacier in a snowstorm without ropes, pick or crampons and loving every minute. I rather loosened up on the conscious positive thinking and visualisation. It was becoming easier to become totally engrossed in a book or in doing something without being selfconscious, without either breaking off to sigh and wonder what was the point of it all or wanting to keep the moment forever. I remember vividly the shock of lying in bed one night and thinking: "I forgot I had cancer today. What am I doing!"

Although I could concentrate on making the best of each day, the future, consciously and unconsciously, was still causing me problems. Right from the beginning I had realised how important it was to believe in and see the future positively. In that first phone call to my parents in New Zealand I had said I intended to get well enough to come home for Christmas and I meant every word, but mostly I avoided thinking about it. For practical purposes it was easier to concentrate on the short term. Subconsciously there must have been doubts. They had the oddest manifestation. I was happy to spend our savings on the holiday in Austria, but I can remember having a great deal of misgivings at buying expensive new mountain waterproofs. That seemed such a waste for one holiday, not a lifetime.

When we came back from holiday, a new college term began for Paul and I too felt able to adjust to going back to work. I had sorted out a job which would be an interesting challenge, but one without lots of tight short term deadlines. It would involve policy review and consider-ative work which I had always preferred to political firefighting. I didn't plan to work normal hours, at least in the beginning. The programme of chemotherapy would give me extra time with the people I cared about too. I felt I was getting quite good at making the most of the oppor-tunities this disease was giving me. I had rather given up on the carrot salads, but I decided that the most that could be said for those extreme diets was that they made people feel better and more energetic and I could do that by eating healthily on my own but more orthodox terms.

I had built up a deep tan from all the time I had spent in the garden over the summer. Lazing in a deck chair reading. Long conversational lunches with friends. That was something else the disease had given me. I had rather taken my friends for granted before. Now I had found out how much they cared for me. I mentally listed all the gains, just like the help yourself books said I should. And yes, I decided I didn't need the cancer to keep the gains, just like they advised. A long and happy life without cancer.

I couldn't just switch off my imagination though. I could also foresee dying and death. In mentally listing all that was positive about my life and about my having cancer I often found myself thinking that dying young could have advantages. I would be surrounded by my family and friends. I would never know the disillusionments of age. I would be remembered as young forever. The thoughts were not welcome. They weren't in the getting well guidebooks. Maybe this was giving in. The golden future might not happen. I might die.

22

I could see the future only as a confusing and continually changing spectrum, everything from complete cure to imminent death. I had never lived with that kind of uncertainty before. My life hadn't been totally predictable but I had felt I knew where I was going and what I would be doing in a few years time. Now I didn't any more and I was frustrated, and frightened.

I could also see a negative side to positive thinking. If it could make me well maybe negative thoughts could make me ill? I was really scared by the possibility. I couldn't stop the negative thoughts even though I wanted to. I told myself that wishful thinking really wasn't likely to make me well. It did make me feel better though. I felt that being as positive as I could about what was happening, trying to find something constructive in all this pain, could keep me sane.

I was trying to keep up the relaxation and meditation, but that was beginning to slip a little too. Visualising the cancer being eaten away by my white cells, doing all the right things in the right order according to the Simonton plan seemed to require such a lot of effort. I'd be dreamily visualising golden fish, then remember they were supposed to have teeth, then that I'd forgotten the eyes. At the end of these meditation sessions I was often anything but relaxed! I was not too upset, swimming was helping me unwind and I was sure my body was keeping the disease under control, after all I felt so well. I spent the day before starting work being my normal extravagant self, buying a winter wardrobe which I had no doubts about needing. It was the first investment in the future I had felt totally comfortable with in months.

The only blot on the landscape was my continuing inability to get the medical information I needed. This had it's ridiculous aspects. I was still not at work so I had no access to the Departmental library. When I did return I was at a remote building with no library facilities anyway. I had got some information about the disease from general books about cancer and a new organisation set up to provide cancer patients with information called BACUP. They were such short simple accounts though and they avoided any discussion about prognosis. I felt I could have written them myself.

There had to be more to the story than this. If all my doctors would do was answer questions then I needed more information in order to know what to ask. None of the general texts could answer the question that had been my main concern since that first morning in hospital. What were my chances of surviving? I knew no one could give me a precise answer but there had to be something more than vague reassurances and evasions. I couldn't accept that dire prognosis I had read in the bookshop. It had to be wrong, didn't it? I was looking partly for the truth, partly for hope. I didn't like to ask my doctors. It was a subject they were obviously avoiding therefore the news must be dreadful. I never seemed to be able to get the right questions out let alone get a real discussion going.

I wanted more. I needed to get hold of those textbooks like the gynaecologist had suggested. All I could think of was the medical sections of Dillons and Foyles bookshops. So one Thursday night I spent a frenetic hour in each of them, furtively leafing through the gynaecology texts. I saw an awful lot of pictures of ovarian tumours in various stages of malignancy and read a number of terse descriptions of the poor prognosis for my kind of disease. It didn't seem very amenable to treatment so didn't seem to arouse much textbook interest. Utter depression and despair. The prognosis now varied between a 3 and 10% chance of five year survival. Again to return to my diary:

It's still two and a half weeks to my next chemotherapy session and I'm spending sleepless nights rehearsing what I want to say. My doctor might not even be there, but be on holiday like everyone else. I know all this, know it's silly to keep playing it over but I can't seem to summon the will to stop. Basically I need to know more about what's happening, to be involved in the decisions rather than challenge them. That stupid bald account I read. Surely it is too simplistic, perhaps outdated? I must know more. Why only one drug for chemotherapy, isn't it usually a cocktail? Are they saving the more toxic for when the cancer comes back? What do they expect to find on the three months assessment? The optimistic scenario and the pessimistic. What will they do? What will it mean for the long term?

It helps to write it down. Perhaps I can get rid of it in the meantime that way. It won't make any difference day by day. My chances are the same no matter what I know. Perhaps better if I know, it will stop me worrying. Surely it can't be worse than that terse account I read, maybe it will be better? I think most of my anxiety is based on my experiences so far. So uptight when I go to the hospital I can't seem to find the opportunity to ask the questions I want, to be assertive. I know they're busy. I just never seem to get the questions out quickly enough. There are always so many other patients waiting. I want to just talk but there's never the time. That's why I relive it over and over, things I might have said, that they might have said ...

Still, my expanding confidence and growing stamina enabled me to get some answers. It wasn't easy. The examination over my doctor turned smartly towards the door. Twice I called her back. The second time I remember saying: "Please. I just don't know enough about what's happening." She finally closed the door and sat down. "What don't you know?" I didn't know what to say. "Everything" seemed to be an exaggeration. I felt stupid. Suddenly I was scared too. Maybe she had a good reason for avoiding the subject. The questions I had been thinking about for weeks were quite forgotten. They all seemed so silly, so trivial. I asked about the survival figures I had read about. They were from preplatinum data. There really was a 50/50 chance after all. If only the chemotherapy would do it's job. Of course it would, I felt so well.

CHAPTER 4

A LONG WINTER

Well you probably guessed how this section begins. The chemotherapy didn't work. After four treatments another laparoscopy showed that there had been no response, if anything I was a little worse. I can still remember the cold shock I felt as my doctor breezily told me the news. I had completely misread her cheerful manner. I couldn't believe it. I wasn't prepared for this. I kept saying, "But I felt so well". My body had let me down again. I couldn't trust what I felt. My experience so far had led me to believe if I felt ill I was ill. Now I was learning you could feel quite well yet be so ill you might die. At least I now had the strength to cope with the extra challenge. Was that evidence of a malevolent fate or a positive plan?

A different form of chemotherapy would be tried. It would make me sicker for longer, I would be in hospital for a week at a time and worst of all, my hair would fall out. Absolutely no question. I would be completely bald within a few weeks of starting treatment.

Now hang on a minute. I wasn't going to accept this without a struggle. I wanted to know more. Again my response to shock was to seek as much information as I could. I suppose it was a way of postponing sheer terror; that would come later. Were there alternatives? Well radiotherapy was possible but very unlikely to work and wouldn't be pleasant either. What was the chance of this working? After all it was similar to the drug which hadn't worked before. About half what it was, about 20/25%. All that for such a slim chance. How long if I did nothing? Maybe six months or a year without symptoms. Did she mean death?

I was learning to think of questions quickly. Maybe alternative treatments could offer me more? That was up to me. I could refuse treatment and take myself off for a "health cure". "We all remember patients who got better despite us rather than because of us". But how shall I tell everyone, they all think I'm getting better", I wailed. I hadn't cried but the shock was having an effect. I wasn't in control of my voice. My doctor was taking time to answer my questions as fully and helpfully as she could and gradually the irrelevant cheerfulness had been replaced by a warmer, less distant manner. She wasn't finding it easy though. She was flushed, awkward, and stood by the door with her arms folded. She suggested I explore the options further by getting a second opinion from a colleague at another hospital.

We escaped for the day. The next morning both Paul and I just called our respective offices to say we weren't going into work. We went for a long walk up and down the cliff tops at Seven Sisters. I still had butterflies in my stomach. I felt more scared than yesterday. I wasn't brave enough to refuse treatment and exclude myself from hospital care altogether. And I wasn't a quitter. O.K. While there was still a chance of cure I'd go for it despite the cost. I couldn't live with myself if I didn't.

What upset me most was not the sickness or the stay in hospital but the thought I was going to lose my hair. It was windy on the cliffs that day. That hurt, I kept thinking this will be the last time, maybe forever, that I'll feel the wind in my hair. My hair was important to my identity. I was vain of it; very thick, dark and shiny it had always been seen as one of my assets. I'd worn it long for years after it was fashionable. I had only had it cut short a few months before as an experimental concession to increasing age. Now I was going to lose it all. I would look different. I would look like a cancer patient. Day in and day out it would remind me. And everyone else. I had only just fully gone back into the world, other people's reactions had always been closely related to the fact that I "seemed so like my normal self." Now I wouldn't any more.

Gradually it sunk in. It wasn't going to be what I had been convincing myself of for the last few months; six months of chemotherapy, then a normal but childless life for ever. I had cancer, maybe I wasn't ever going to recover. The chances were much slimmer now. Even if I did get better, it was going to be a long hard struggle through the winter. No opportunity to go home to my family now.

I began to realise that cancer is not an acute illness. You may not necessarily be cured or die quickly. I had to face the fact that this was a chronic condition. Nothing was ever going to be the same again. When I had said that to myself in June, I meant the diagnosis had shattered my expectations, my vision of myself, my previously charmed existence. I felt I had lost my innocence and been forced to face grim reality for the first time in my life. I began to see that I was going to have to live with that reality for ever. Uncertainty stretched far ahead.

I got information on how to cope with hair loss from BACUP and bought myself some scarves to cope with the moulting stage. I also bought two wigs from Selfridges, two because I liked one which "made me look like a civil servant", and Paul liked one which he said made me look trendy and I said made me look like a muppet. Another one, plainer but suitable for everyday, was a gift from the NHS. There were lots of jokes and good humour but nothing took away the pain.

I played with the wigs, convinced myself they were an improvement as my own hair began to look flat and lifeless and fall out after the first treatment. I shrieked when I washed my hair, took my head out of the basin and found it still full of now unattached hair. I knew I was vulnerable in water. I had visions of my hair streaming off behind me as I swam down the swimming pool. I wore a cap and worked out elaborate strategies of how to get from wig to cap and back again without terrorising the other swimmers and embarrassing myself by having to reveal my baldness.

And the awfulness of having to be in hospital on that ward all that time. And the sickness. Vomiting for days at a time. The anti-sickness drugs never worked.

The staff, the nurses and housemen who I got to know very well over the next few months, were universally kind; some were very kind indeed. I remember many of them still. The young nurse who tiptoed into my darkened room at 3am to put an arm round me as the vomiting began. "God it's awful isn't it" she said. She sat and chatted for a bit and then left saying "Just buzz if you want me to sit with you. I wish I could help." Then there was the houseman who produced a comic novel from his pocket to cheer me through the day I had stopped being sick but felt too ill to be interested in anything.

It was a very intimate relationship. I was vulnerable. Some of them shared their vulnerability with me in return. One houseman sat on my bed for a chat in the sleepless early hours. He sighed and told me how difficult he found me as a patient. "All my training is to make people better. You come in here so well and I make you ill." I was grateful to him for sharing the thought. He made me feel I was still a human being.

My fellow patients could be a pain though. I heard rumours of other cancer patients but I never saw any except for a couple of old ladies in their 80s. All we had in common was gynaecological cancer, or as one of them put it, "a problem down there". I was told with relish about a young woman with breast cancer one morning; that she had died in the night and caused a great disturbance which mercifully I slept through. It was still mostly elderly diabetics I met and tried to be civil to.

A few of the patients I met had a more profound effect. I realised how privileged and protected I had been. I had never come across real ongoing chronic illness before. I saw disability and pain lasting not weeks or months but years with no hope of cure. They taught me there are worse illnesses than cancer.

It wasn't all bad. I still had the same stubbornness which had seen me through so far and I learned to cope and make the best I could out of this too. I tried to see my week in hospital as a warm and peaceful oasis, a week out of the hurly burly of the rest of the month when life continued at a rather frantic pace and I tried to pack into two or three weeks what might normally have taken all four.

The first day in hospital was never too bad, I was only in for hydration, monitoring input and output of liquid. Attached to a drip but with no other restriction provided a vein could be found in my left arm and my right was free to write. Writing was a means of escaping from my immediate surroundings. I was too anxious, too easily distracted, to read with my usual concentration. So I used the day as an opportunity to write the letters home I hadn't had time for in the previous weeks. These letters had become more frequent in the months of convalescence and it was a habit I wanted to preserve.

I made sure I had plenty of new books to read and some favourite music to listen to. I had been given a little personal stereo before my first visit to hospital. It became a lifeline. I learned to give myself a new tape or two before each chemotherapy session, something to look forward to. Nothing could take away the sickness of the first few days after treatment. They were two days to be endured. But after that even if I couldn't eat I could read and shut myself away with my music, though I was always pretty drowsy thanks to the anti-sickness drugs. It was a time to be alone. I didn't want visitors. I couldn't make the effort. By the time I left hospital each time I was able to eat a bit, then the sickness would gradually lessen and a few days later I would be starving. In the two to three weeks each month I was quite well I ate like a horse, gradually I was regaining the weight I had lost in the weeks after the initial surgery.

The weeks seemed to go by very quickly. Even the few days convalescence after getting out of hospital had many pleasures, lazy days listening to music and reading with a deliberate treat at the end before going back to work; an afternoon theatre matinee, lunch with a friend. Then back into the swing of things.

Work was demanding but satisfying, most of the time. But there were odd days when I stopped in my tracks and thought: "What am I doing? Why am I wasting what little time is left on such trivial issues? Does it really matter whether I, here and now, find a solution to this? Will anything I ever do in this Department really change lives for the better?" There were times when it all felt very unreal and the constant shifting of focus from patient to civil servant was hard to achieve. By and large though I found the same pleasure I always had in getting to grips with a problem and working out the best solution; more, because for the first time I was quite free to concentrate on the work I found most satisfying and to work at my own pace. I was working normally, I was treated so normally that some days I wanted to say "take it easy I'm an invalid you know!"

There were days when I genuinely looked forward to the time around the next chemotherapy treatment as a lazy respite. It was an important image when I was well, an image never really dispelled by the reality of sickness. Despite being unwell there was something attractive about being able to completely and safely surrender in hospital. I didn't need to make an effort any more. I could just be ill. It was one of the few lapses in concentration I allowed myself in the constant fight to get and stay well. I didn't need to worry about anything, either the important or the trivial. Either whether I would survive or what we would eat for dinner and whether I had remembered the cat food.

Life outside hospital continued fairly normally. As much as possible my colleagues were avoiding putting pressure on me, but a real job with real responsibilities inevitably meant some urgent demands. I still had time for a good lunch break most days; a long discussion, not necessarily about me or my disease, with one of my friends. Their support, and more, just the everyday contact with them all, was an important link with reality. My late-ish starts in the morning meant I had quarter of an hour most days to practice my meditation, though I think the main help to relaxation was that it kept me at home till after the main rush hour.

Not losing my hair helped. I still looked like I had always done. I had carefully prepared the way with a lot of jokes about wigs. Flurries of long black hair followed me everywhere, and I still shrieked every time I washed it. The basin was still regularly filled with hair. It was looking a bit thin, but nothing more dramatic happened. After six weeks or so of this I asked my doctors how long it would take to all fall out and they told me it probably wasn't going to now. "In about 30% of cases it doesn't. We had to tell you it did so you would adjust". ADJUST! Did they know what I went through! I still wish I had had the courage to rage at them. Instead I imagined presenting them with the Selfridges bill for two unworn wigs which I would never have bought if I hadn't been assured of complete baldness within weeks.

Life wasn't all work. I continued to make time for and gain a lot from my friends. We grew even closer and enjoyed so many more good times together than we would normally have had. Paul and I did new things together. We borrowed the daughter of our best friends for a weekend, took her to the zoo, spoiled her rotten and had a marvellously exhausting time. We rediscovered the pleasures of the theatre, though booking ahead through the uncertainties of treatment was sometimes difficult and I was often too tired in the evenings after work to cope with an evening out as well.

I was making the most of what strength I had. The physical training programme continued. The weather was no longer very good for tennis; squash, my usual substitute, often felt a bit more than I could manage. But the swimming continued. Ten lengths the first time after treatment, but sixteen by the morning of the day I was to go in for the next bout. A swim was my rather eccentric way of surviving the boredom and tension to come. It wasn't always easy. I remember once going the day after I came out of hospital. I can still remember the nightmarish sensation of swimming but getting nowhere, I just had no strength at all.

On rereading all this sounds unbelievably positive. My perception has changed. I now remember my hospital stay less as a peaceful safe haven. I remember more the utter tedium of feeling ill, too sick to concentrate on diversion but not sick enough to escape in sleep.

If anyone asked me now how I felt about chemotherapy I think I'd be more likely to say "It was ruddy awful. I was in hospital for a week, threw up for days at time and only really lived an ordinary life two and a half weeks in every four". Same events, different attitude. That was genuinely not how I felt at the time. The challenge, the need to make the best of things or go insane with self pity, brought out a resilience I didn't know I had. I just instinctively refused to dwell on the down side of what I was going through. This was not a front for others, I was fighting so hard I rarely admitted negative feelings even to myself.

I thought I was doing quite well those first few months in maintaining "real life" between doses of what I was unable to refer to as anything but "the poison". There are limits to positive thinking and I found it impossible to regard this chemotherapy as more than a necessary evil towards a possible good. No more images of a beautiful liquid soothing away the cancer now.

I discovered more was possible thanks to my doctor. I had told her, before I started the new chemotherapy regime, that I was a New Zealander and wanted to go home for Christmas. She remembered and asked me one day in November, "What about that trip down under?" I just looked at her, completely taken aback. "Abandoned", I said bleakly. It had been one of the biggest disappointments of the whole setback. "I don't see why it should be" she said. "You can have treatment out there, I'll arrange it. Think about it. If you're well enough to go you should." Was it really possible?

Well God owed me a favour, and the next day we had booked two of the last three seats on any available flight between then and Christmas. I rang New Zealand to a chorus of delighted surprise, my father muttering that he was in need of a large brandy.

We had a glorious six weeks, not least because we exchanged New Zealand midsummer for one of the bitterest winters England had seen in years. I spent many long lazy days with my family, just enjoying time together. It was pleasant in itself and it healed some of the panic I had felt at the diagnosis, "but I haven't seen my family for three years!" Neither side was I hope saying goodbye, but there was a peace between us that I certainly hadn't experienced with my parents before. I had time to get to know other members of my family, more opportunities than there otherwise would have been to get to know them intimately. I took much pleasure in their company and that of our old friends. We may not have kept up with them on a regular basis but they are such good friends that it doesn't matter. However many years apart we always start exactly where we left off.

I wallowed in homesickness. Real sea, crashing surf. Clear blue skies, windy cliffs and long sandy beaches with no one else in sight. Lying in bed at night and hearing the faint sound of the waves. The tall bare mountains of Central Otago. The lush quiet of native fern and beech forest. Sparkling streams, deep rivers glinting green. I missed it all so much. Not enough to give up my life in England, but I needed to renew my connection with it all. I couldn't return, it would be like going back to childhood, but I needed to acknowledge it's place at the centre of my life.

It was reassuring for my family, I think, to see me looking so well despite the disease and the months of treatment. On the other hand they also had to adjust to the reality of what I was going through. They insisted on seeing me in hospital, witnessing for themselves the vomiting, the tubes and the drip. There was more to their reaction than I ever got to know about. I remember vividly an incident which demonstrated how fragile the normality was. One evening in the course of a friendly family squabble my father says he told me to "drop dead". It was an exhortation he had often used to shut up his unruly children. I didn't register the significance of what he had said, nor did anyone else, but the poor man later confessed to spending a sleepless night worrying about his tactlessness.

Although chemotherapy interrupted the holiday, it was soon over and within a week I was climbing mountains again. There were many expeditions of that kind; even an attempt at white water rafting. There's nothing like careering down rapids in a rubber raft to make you concentrate on the moment rather than the long term future! I loved it but suspect I would never have tried it except for the cancer. The thought that I had nothing to lose was giving me a certain confidence. Another gain to be notched up. Mind you there was a lot of muttering that I had let Paul get me into some dumb things but this had to be the dumbest. I guess there was a certain element of defiance. My kidney function was reduced which meant the drug dosage had to be lessened too; now there was even less chance of a cure. To some extent I was proving to myself and everyone else that there was absolutely nothing wrong with me thank you.

There were still sometimes shadowed edges to what were very genuine pleasures. The heightened awareness, a sheer joy in being alive, had stayed with me since those sunny days in the garden just after my first release from hospital. What produced that wonderful intensity was the reminder I had had that it wasn't going to last forever. Sometimes that could mean that even, perhaps especially, when most conscious of how glad I was to be spending time with friends or family I was also aware that we might never have this opportunity again. That poignancy had never been far from the surface in the early days. Then while on holiday in Austria, and in getting back to work, it had diminished and I was more genuinely able to enjoy each day comfortably.

With the increased uncertainty of the more intense chemotherapy it had returned but my attitude to that self consciousness was changing. Now it was beginning to be a bore. I was willing to give up the intensity to regain something of the ability to take life for granted again. I felt I had lost a certain innocence. Everything had become much too significant. It wasn't just the links with the future I was conscious of, but the past as well. I couldn't live entirely at the moment. There were so many reminders of previous happinesses in sometimes quite trivial things. I couldn't just be happy, I kept thinking how happy I was. I wasn't simply living, I was watching myself too. It made me feel I was acting, that maybe my reactions weren't real.

The uncertainty also produced other tensions sometimes. Should I still be determining choices and priorities on the basis that time was precious and I had to make the most of every opportunity, or could I afford to relax? Making the most of every opportunity could sometimes be exhausting. Should I be looking to my long term career prospects or concentrating on just doing a decent days work day by day? It was easy enough to see myself achieving long term goals but the way forward was less clear when goals required choices and sacrifices here and now.

The holiday in New Zealand was happy, but the sense of completion it gave me was disturbing. The intense distress I had felt that my life was going to be over before I had achieved anything had produced a lot of soul searching and many mental lists of what was positive about my life so far. I felt a need to develop some of my relationships, for I had come to the conclusion that the extent to which my living impinged on someone else was the only legacy I would ever have. I saw any success as completion rather than open ended progress. It created a superstitious fear that if my life was complete maybe God was trying to get me used to the idea that I was going to die.

One rather strange incident disturbed me a great deal and perhaps illustrates the point. Shortly before I left New Zealand I had been contacted by a friend who was in London that year on sabbatical from his university post in New Zealand. We had known each other well as undergraduates and as PhD students in London years before. For a reason he still cannot explain, he went one evening to a seminar for visiting lecturers and, to cut a long story short, met an American Fellow who had been searching for me for the last three years to discuss my thesis and whether he could quote it extensively in a book he was writing. We met and I found out that my work had not simply been gathering dust on the library shelves. It had started a thriving cottage industry in related studies and was now of interest to government agencies and academics on both sides of the Atlantic. High on my list of wasted efforts in those early days had been the years spent writing that thesis. I tried to accept it as a straightforward piece of good news but I don't believe in coincidence, I much prefer the description "God acting anonymously". What did it all mean? Was this God's attempt at a consolation prize before delivering the final blow?

The holiday was over all too soon and we came back to the same mix of ups and downs, health and sickness, home, work and hospital as before.

Yet another laparoscopy shortly after I returned showed that I was responding to treatment at last. I was "better" but my wanting to quantify the change was unrealistic. "We can't stick a ruler down the laparoscopy tube can we?" Exhilaration, followed three weeks later by despair. I had the sudden insight to challenge my doctor, that her evasiveness had meant that it hadn't got much better, and found myself to be right.

That was about the worst outpatients episode ever. I still don't know whether it was due to some external cause or whether it was related in some way to my doctor's concern about my not responding well to treatment.

The appointment did not begin well. I had the usual unexplained long wait. I became very conscious that I was no longer the competent individual I had been when I walked in, I was a patient again.

I was fed up. I had been carefully rehearsing all my questions for days but after an hour and a half just sitting there I wanted to go home. Did they do this deliberately so I wouldn't ask questions or did they just not realise how it felt? I hadn't been able to relax. No one had told me it was going to be a long wait so I didn't dare go and get a cup of coffee. No one had said anything except "go and take a seat under the clock". I never could work out the system. There were always lots of other patients waiting but sometimes I got seen quickly and sometimes I seemed to be at the end of the queue. I tried to read but I couldn't concentrate, wondering all the time whether I would be next.

At last I was shown into an examination room and told to undress. Not long to wait now I thought. My doctor was just outside the door talking to a young man in a white coat. They smiled vaguely at me. I sat on the couch, feeling cold and very much alone. I heard them walk past. Oh no. There was still another patient to see already stripped and waiting too. I heard fragments of the conversation through the wall. It was getting late. Would they have time for all my questions? Footsteps again; but they continued past my door and back to the desk.

Wait a minute, my doctor was talking about me! "A girl, referred for infertility". "Girl" said a lot about our relationship, we weren't that different in age. And were they again refusing to acknowledge all those months of what is still the worst pain I've ever known? She began to talk about what had happened to me. "We just don't know whether aspirating that cyst caused it to spread around the abdomen". I felt sick and shaky. I had known this was theoretically a possibility but no one had actually talked about it before. I wanted to open the door and shout "It's me you're talking about". Mercifully she began to lower her voice a little. I continued to wait.

At last she came in with the young man and continued to talk to him about me. I wanted to challenge her but I wasn't brave enough. Besides,

I needed all my assertion for the essentials. I asked about the laparoscopy and was deeply shocked by the answer I hadn't been able to work out for myself. I carried on to ask what such a poor response meant in terms of final outcome. Was there any chance still of a complete remission? She said she didn't know. I can't remember now what I said but I obviously asked the same question in a different way. She shrieked at me "I just don't know. You're trying to back me into a corner and I refuse!"

It was a real low point. I was beginning to feel I'd had enough. I confessed that I was beginning to get a bit weary of it all, the uncertainty, the sickness; I just wanted it to go away so I could get on with my life. This wasn't playing by the rules. We had a funny little routine. My doctor normally asked me "Bowels OK? Waterworks OK? Coping OK?" I normally laughed and said "Yes, yes and yes". She looked rather taken aback. "Well we all want that. You're alive and well at least." I gave up. She obviously hadn't a clue.

By the end of the appointment I was deeply distressed. Still charming to my doctor of course, but I quivered with rage all the way home. I was angry with myself more than anything. Why had I been such a rabbit, a patient. No one else would have been able to get away with treating me like that. I was due at a friend's for dinner. Paul found me pacing the dark street outside, close to tears and unable to go in and act normally.

The experience had one positive outcome. I vowed I wouldn't be caught out again. I was now sufficiently assertive to get a straight answer to a straight question, but that wasn't enough if you didn't ask the right question in the first place. I had just learnt that if you asked the wrong question you could end up with a misleading answer. I was fearful that I might be ignorant of whole areas where I just didn't know enough to ask questions at all. I needed information, every medical detail I could lay my hands on.

At last I was back in the main Departmental building with access to the library. I started to read. There were very few oncology texts, and fewer journals. Those few gave me a couple of references which I blithely requested the staff to seek from other libraries. I received some odd looks but no direct challenge. I started to understand more about the disease and realised how little I knew about my own case. I remembered the vital words of the pathologists report, "serous, moderately differentiated". Yes but what grade, the textbooks said grade was important. Had there been any ascites present? That was an important prognostic indicator. I needed to talk to my doctor. But how? I'd been trying for a year with precious little success.

At this point my GP intervened. He heard from Paul that I was turning to textbooks in frustration and became concerned. When he heard a little more he kindly offered to speak to my doctor himself.

Well the next outpatients appointment was definitely sticky. My doctors marched in, gynaecologist and two nurses in tow. (Nurses? I'd never had nurses before.) They all looked stern and the underlings were obviously under instruction to stay for the whole appointment. But I was too frustrated to be intimidated and I had brought Paul with me for moral support. I had spent the previous evening talking over with him exactly what I wanted to know. He helped out when I stopped for breath. I got my discussion and by now was well read enough to keep it going for almost an hour. I managed to miss a few points, and was reminded of them with a certain flourish, but a dialogue was finally established.

What we discussed mainly was where we might go from here if the chemotherapy hadn't worked. My second six months of treatment were at last coming to an end. None of the prospects seemed very attractive, all that we were discussing involved even more intensive hospital treatment. After the last chemotherapy and before the evaluating laparoscopy we escaped for a week. We went to Sorrento in Southern Italy, a wicked and delightful extravagance.

Lovely golden weather. Old favourite haunts and new spots on Capri. Picnicking on the cliffs around Sorrento. "Yes that's the path Signore but it doesn't go anywhere". "What's the Italian for that's the whole point?" We excitedly explored the ruins of Pompeii and Herculaneum. We found Cuma and Lake Avernus on the basis of a very crude sketch map and Paul's even sketchier knowledge of Book Six of the Aeneid. It was fun and proof that I was alive in every sense.

Then back to the news. I was virtually unchanged from the situation I had been in at the beginning. No better, perhaps very slightly worse.

35

CHAPTER 5
WHERE DO WE GO FROM HERE?

I was intensely disappointed. It had responded a little initially, why didn't it continue? All that pain, that vomiting, had been for nothing. It really was for nothing. My doctor told me that it was more likely I had stayed well in spite of rather than because of the chemotherapy. If the cancer had stabilised something else must have caused it, maybe my stubbornness. My doctor was sceptical but was unable to come up with a better explanation. It was encouraging and worrying at the same time. What happened if I stopped being stubborn? Surely there must be more to it than that.

I was defiant. I spent the two days "recovering" from the laparoscopy getting down to the spring cleaning I hadn't done for the last year and giving the garden a good going over. There was absolutely nothing wrong with me! But natural sloth and sanity soon took over.

Where do we go from here was the burning question. The dialogue I had established with my doctor helped. There was no holding back of information now. Again the discussion lasted for a good half hour. She seemed to be trying to make amends for her brusqueness over the last year. "Very few patients go to the trouble you have done to get the information to be able to ask these questions. They just don't want to know." I didn't debate the point. Perhaps they just didn't have the opportunities and bloodymindedness I did. I concentrated on my own case.

We discussed the more intensive options fully, but at this stage she didn't know whether they were feasible. They all sounded daunting. One had a ten per cent mortality rate from the treatment alone. Subsequent inquiries found that none were suitable.

Paul asked her whether there was any real chance now of my being cured. My doctor hesitated, looking at me, trying to guess whether I wanted to know the answer. Realistically, she said, we were now looking for ways to slow down the growth of the cancer but cure was most unlikely. I knew anyway. It was still unexpectedly shocking to hear her say it. I wasn't quite as prepared for the news as I thought. My voice started to quaver a little as we discussed other options.

I could try high doses of hormones: "they may do you some good and they'll do you no harm". Great. I wanted more than this. I was 32 and in perfect health. There had to be something more. To hear that cure was impossible from someone else might help me accept it. It would settle too the nagging little doubt that maybe somewhere, somehow there would be something we could try.

I had been a little worried for some time. How could I be sure that she really knew all the possibilities, all the experiments that were going on. My doctor treated people with many different kinds of cancer, so did the other doctors at the hospital. How could she save the time to know everything which might be going on in my field? The hospital wasn't a specialist cancer centre. Maybe someone somewhere was doing something that would help. My mother was always sending me cuttings from her local newspaper about this or that new breakthrough in cancer treatment. Sometimes it included a frustratingly vague reference to advances in the treatment of ovarian cancer. There were lots of references to what was happening in America. Was I missing out? I knew these were the kind of newspaper reports my doctor would probably dismiss as journalistic exaggeration. But maybe somehow, someway, I was missing something? I didn't want her to feel I was doubting her competence but how could one person know everything? Maybe if I saw someone else, other doctors from more specialist units, I would maximise my chances of coming across that magical new development. I knew it was probably a fruitless quest for a non-existent holy grail but I had to know. It was my life at stake after all.

One of the doctors she consulted about experimental options offered to talk to me. He had already said he had nothing to recommend other than hormones either. My own doctor assumed this meant that I would have no need to talk to him, but she was wrong. And I wanted more. I started from the same point she said she did, that there were no definitive options. In one sense it was reassuring that her colleague had suggested hormones, in another it was worrying. Maybe they were too similar in approach.

Another doctor I had been to for a second opinion several months before had said then we could try more chemotherapy if this lot failed. Maybe she could offer me an alternative, or help me accept there was nothing more by recommending hormones as well. I agonized over the point. Maybe it would seem like I distrusted my own doctor if I suggested this too. I carefully rehearsed over and over what I would say. Of course when it came to confrontation I was again a marshmallow. "I don't think you should go and see both. You're in danger of getting so much information you won't be able to handle it." (What did she mean? Had she still not grasped there was a brain underneath my mild manner? Or was she warning me I might find the doctors disagreed. Fine. It would open up a debate as to why a given option was better.) Tension does not help me to be articulate. "But I want to go" I stammered. "Well I don't think you should". "But I want to" I insisted. She offered me a compromise. To go and see the doctor who recommended the hormones first, then, if I still wanted to, to see the other. I accepted reluctantly. How long was all that going to take?

Quite a long time I found out. The first doctor wasn't able to see me for a month. My heart in my mouth I rang back again. My doctor was busy. I left a message with her secretary explaining I wanted to talk about arranging an appointment with the second doctor now in view of the delay. I got a message back to say OK. Things were at last looking up.

I was feeling better too. More than two months now without chemotherapy. So I wasn't cured but I was well. I was beginning to accept that, and appreciate what it meant. Again there was a period of what I remember as intensely sensual enjoyment. I was not used to the joy of being alive striking me as I hurried for a train on a sunny morning. A work morning at that! And I felt so well! For the first time in two years I had no monthly trauma of pain and vomiting to go through. I hadn't realised just how ill I had been before the diagnosis or how much the treatment had knocked me out until it's relentless rhythm stopped.

I returned to full time work but I began to miss the space that the chemotherapy weeks had given me. I found I had some psychological recovering to do as well. I was just about coping with all the bank holidays, but beginning to feel very tired. Right. This was no way to carry on. The choices were much more clear cut now. If I was unlikely to get better there was no question of putting up with something out of deference to long term goals. I arranged to cut down to four days work a week. That gave me just the right balance. A little more time for myself, but still enough to feel fully part of things at work.

And I finally got to see the doctor who had recommended hormone treatment. What a revelation that was. His attitude and his manner were so different to what I had been used to. I had again carefully rehearsed all my questions but this time there was no need. Information was freely given. I remember he began by taking my history and saying: "Let me explain what I think is happening to you." Some deep anxiety relaxed. It was almost a physical sensation. I didn't need to ask the "right" questions. Explanations were being volunteered. He seemed to have all the time in the world. I didn't need to hurry. We instantly established a rapport in a way that I hadn't succeeded in doing in all those months with my own doctor. It was easy to do so. He actually seemed interested in me, not just my disease.

His whole outpatient system made communication easier. No lonely wait in an examination room, dressed only in my petticoat, this time. He allowed me to talk to him with my clothes on, making the physical examination deliberately separate. It was even held in a different room. The business of discussion was taken seriously here, not fitted in between pokes and prods. Paul was invited in to share the consultation as a matter of course. Here, unlike my own hospital, this seemed to be a part of the normal routine.

The attitude of the other staff, the nurses who came and chatted to put me at ease, was so different. Even the receptionist was friendly. There seemed to be just as many patients waiting to be seen but a good deal less nervous tension. Patients were invited in one by one; not lined up in the examination rooms waiting for their doctors to appear. The clinic was running a little behind here too, but the receptionist warned me of that and with profuse apologies sent me off for a cup of tea. I felt like a human being, not a patient.

There was no more treatment to offer me, but that didn't matter. This doctor managed to be hopeful about the future possibilities. Nothing had really changed, but I came away so much more confident. He also invited me to a weekend seminar for patients and their relatives discussing ways they might help themselves. I had finally found a doctor interested in these things which had been so important to me. As we talked, I realised we had similar views. He had rejected those "alternative" practices I had found hard to take, but was evidently as interested in the psychological aspects as I was. I needed no persuading, after all I was sure there was plenty more I could learn. I could hardly wait for the seminar which would be in six weeks time.

I walked out of the hospital that afternoon confident and happy. A few hours later anger set in. All that pain I had suffered at my own hospital now seemed so needless. And the anger grew. By the following day I had to do something. I would write it out. I had spoken long and eloquently to my friends about the shortcomings of my usual hospital. They had told me I ought to write about my experiences but I didn't want to be the author of yet another patient's story of NHS horrors. I wanted to change what I saw as wrong. Now I had the mechanism I needed to get across my points by contrasting the two doctors and their regimes. I spent the afternoon writing frenziedly. I tried the draft on a few friends. A good read they said, and it needs saying. I wasn't quite satisfied that it was ready for public view and I continued working on it.

I had other things to occupy me anyway. Another round in the battle with the hospital. The appointment with the third doctor hadn't yet been made. I had another long and humiliating hassle to get an appointment to see my doctor for a check up. I was getting very angry indeed. My relationship with my doctor was costing me too much time and energy again; for the first time in many months I was writing long agonized screeds in my diary. Obsessively thinking about what I said, would say, might have said. What she said, would say and might have said in reply. Again I was so hurt because I couldn't reconcile the kindness and obvious concern of the long discussion we had had after the laparoscopy results with the subsequent put down.

Why didn't I do as all my friends kept advising and simply change to the other hospital. It wasn't that easy. Although we had communication difficulties I knew my doctor cared what happened and that sort of relationship took time. Then, just as my direction seemed clear, it all went into reverse. I saw the third doctor, she now agreed chemotherapy had nothing more to offer me. A few weeks later I saw my own doctor again. The discussion was long and friendly. I could accept hormone treatment now. The second opinion doctor had been so much more hopeful. It was still experimental treatment but he had known patients who had gone into complete remission on it. He pointed out that something more aggressive could still be tried if or as soon as the disease got worse. The important thing was to keep a careful watch over me. I had nothing to lose by trying it. I talked it over with my own doctor. Communication was at last two way between us. It felt as if she was listening to me for the first time.

She didn't apologise but at least conceded my anxiety about her refusal to see me. I even plucked up enough courage to tell her how impressed I had been by the set up at the second hospital. I wasn't sure it really sank in though, and I joined in her laughter when I said having to hold a conversation while undressed was intimidating. It turned out that maybe she had an interest in the psychology of this disease after all. At one point she just threw into the conversation: "Some people find visualisation helpful". I was too stunned to reply. She was interested in this side of it? Why on earth had she never said anything before?

All in all it was the friendliest, most relaxed and discursive meeting we had ever had. Appointments continued on the same basis. I wrote:

She isn't a monster, even the worst incidents took place in an atmosphere of breezy cheerfulness and friendly smiles. I have had many instances of her caring concern but over the last few months this has become much more evident. Is it just that my diminishing anxiety makes me easier to deal with? Or has she come to the conclusion that as there is nothing she can do for me she will just be nice to me? I feel there is more to it than that, that she has changed too. Maybe she has finally realised how hurtful her brusqueness can be. I have always suspected it might be related to her very concern anyway. Whatever the motive I bask in the outcome. I'm not entirely sure of her yet, and continue to take Paul with me because somehow his presence seems to be linked to this change of attitude. Being able to trust in her concern has had quite a profound effect though and is I think related to my growing confidence and general well being.

There was more to life than hospitals anyway. My brother and new sister in law had recently arrived from Australia, and what with playing hostess, keeping up with work and still seeing as much as I could of my friends there was not a lot of time to spare.

Part of me was very weary of all the questioning, all the struggle. I finally began to accept that maybe there wasn't a lot more medicine could do for me. I'd resisted that knowledge for so long that when I finally faced it it had lost it's power. I was beginning to abandon my obsession with numbers; survival rates, response rates and percentages. Maybe I was just deluding myself, but the strange thing was it didn't seem to matter. The initial reaction to the knowledge that chemotherapy hadn't worked had been sheer panic. Hence the frantic hassles to see all the doctors and get all the information I could. Eventually I had to accept that there was little else to be done, at least in the meantime.

There was a certain amount of relief at the end of such a wide angle of uncertainty between complete cure and death. I realised that a lot of anxious stress had been caused by the constant shifting of focus between the possibility of a near normal lifespan and an imminent end. For the last year the alternatives seemed to be constantly changing between complete recovery and death before Christmas. Now it seemed the field had narrowed. Chances were the disease would kill me, the question was would it be soon or years hence. Hope was still very much alive but concentrated on postponing the end as long as possible. There was a lot of potential there. I might have lost any realistic possibility of cure but so too had I lost the assumption that if it wasn't getting better it must be getting worse. Tense uncertainty was giving way to a calmer and more concentrated fight against a known enemy.

Quite suddenly a lot of pain had vanished. I was at last content to just enjoy the moment and to focus completely on it. I had finally learned to accept that the only reality was what was happening here and now. I found I was quite genuinely beginning to take each day as it came and for what it could give, to enjoy it and make the most of it without worrying about the future. Without too the resonances of the past, and the fear that happy times might never come again. I was genuinely not very worried about the future. I felt I had been through all that. I had been forced to do most of the grieving for the life I would never have those first few days after the diagnosis. In the time since I had had a chance to make some completions and adjustments. I didn't want to die, I still felt it to be a pointless waste, but I didn't fear it. Either it was going to be another interesting experience or it was going to be a nothingness, either way I didn't see it as anything to fear. Nor did I need to seek cosmic significances. It didn't matter if my work was never going to make any changes that couldn't be made just as well if not better by someone else. I was happy to go through the motions, to see the pleasures in the activity without worrying about the outcome.

There was still some pain though. I had lost the worry about the future but the past was beginning to creep up on me. Writing the article really started it off I suppose, though even before then the euphoria of the first few weeks after chemotherapy had started to wear thin. What had started off as a fairly intellectual exercise became an emotional one as I began to think about those early days that had caused me so much pain, so much needless pain. I had been too busy coping with it all to really allow myself to come to terms with it as it happened.

It was in this rather mixed up state that I went on the weekend seminar for cancer patients and their relatives and friends. My sure sense that this was the right thing to do started to become a little shaky that first evening. After all I had never joined a support group before. I had refused to let cancer define me. I was going to be different to other cancer patients. Now I had signed up for a whole weekend with a group of people whose only point in common was that they had cancer. The group aspect bothered me too. I am not a natural extrovert. I was quite happy to share my thoughts about having cancer with my closest friends and family. But in a group of twenty strangers!

I wasn't won over immediately. We finally found another couple in the bar who looked as lost as we were. "Are you with the uh .. group?" It turned out that they were, the ice was broken and it seemed we had more in common than our disease. After dinner we started the first session. Sitting round in a circle; we were all asked to introduce ourselves. I was shaking. No one else seemed as shy and nervous as I was. I was angry with myself. Why this hang up? I was perfectly confident in other situations. It came to my turn, I was able to mumble a sentence and the panic passed. But I wasn't sure about this, we didn't seem to be going anywhere very quickly. Talking about lack of control as the great fear, that didn't worry me. What about death? Was that taboo here too? Ideas and frustrations turned through my head all night. I didn't sleep.

The next two days are rather a blur. I remember intensely nervous anxiety to understand myself, what was being said and how I fitted into it all. No taboo subjects now. Another sleepless night, mostly spent sitting in the bathroom while Paul slept, writing down all the thoughts I hadn't expressed in the open session. I began to realise how confused I was about how I felt but I had begun to see too that writing it out could be helpful. After all I earned my living by my powers of pen and analysis. Why not use these skills for myself?

During the course of the weekend patients and their supporters talked openly about their fears and anxieties. We were gently led to an understanding of how we might cope with them more easily by learning to relax, gain energy through fun and creativity and make the most of the support of family and friends. We also had more factual sessions where we talked about what cancer was and how it was treated, and about the importance of keeping ourselves fit and well through diet and exercise. Nothing I couldn't accept. We weren't being deluded with unrealistic hopes of certain cure, but being advised on how we might practically improve the quality of our lives. When diet was first mentioned I had a momentary qualm. "Oh no, he's one of those," I thought. I was wrong. What were being recommended were no more than orthodox guidelines on healthy eating.

I was already familiar with much of the information and some of the techniques. I had after all been avidly reading anything I could get my hands on for the last year. It had been a lonely and at times distressing journey. My eventual decision to refuse to have anything to do with weird diets and bogus science had not been an easy one. It was an incredible relief to finally find someone, a cancer doctor firmly within the medical establishment what is more, who agreed with my conclusions.

I still learned much that was new as regards strategies and techniques that weekend. I had for example tried relaxation and meditation before, but over time the practice had slipped. Simply doing it again made me appreciate it's potential. I was persuaded to expand my horizons too. I had tried and rejected imaginative visualisation a long time ago but actually trying it out again with everyone else renewed my interest. I benefitted too from the discussion of concepts and psychological processes I had only dimly and intuitively been aware of until then.

I would not have considered seeking out psychiatric help myself. I didn't think I was disturbed enough to need therapy. But during the course of the weekend I discovered there was more to psychology than crisis help for the insane. The weekends were jointly run by a gifted psychotherapist who was also an exciting teacher. I began a journey of self discovery that it continuing still. There were psychological aspects to this disease, and to life itself, which I hadn't found in my reading so far. I rediscovered old interests in philosophy. It was like being a young student again, earnestly talking about the meaning of life and death. It wasn't morbid, it was exhilarating.

The excitement of discovery and sense of control was I think even greater among those who had no acquaintance with the concept of self help beforehand. Some patients had only recently been diagnosed, and I was very aware of their initial desperation giving way to confident hope. If only I could have received this help then how much easier it would have been I thought. None of that agonizing, that desperate and bewildering attempt to sift the fringe from the common sense. Few patients were lucky enough to have my stamina. They ought to be able to rely on their doctors to help.

I began to realise how much I had changed since the year before. Then I had begun exploring alternative therapies looking for the cure my doctors could not promise me. Now I lacked that fiery determination I saw in some of the newly diagnosed patients. I wasn't so sure I believed in miracles any more but I certainly felt better for changing my lifestyle and for feeling that there was something I could do to help myself. It would do me no harm and might help me to live longer. I couldn't lose. It would certainly improve the quality of my life. It worried me a little. Getting rid of cancer no longer seemed to be my highest priority. Maybe I was adjusting too well? I remember feeling shocked and a little guilty after the first visualisation exercise. We were supposed to imagine containing and disposing of a problem. I can't remember what mine was, but unlike the other patients, it wasn't cancer.

It was not just patients who benefitted. By the end of the weekend Paul was totally enthusiastic. "This isn't about coping with cancer. It's about coping with life. Everyone should have the opportunity to do this" was his verdict. Until now, attention and support had been focused on me, the patient. He had begun to realise just how much the strain of coping with me, and with his anxieties about the possibility of my death, had taken from his own life, sapping his energy and creativity. He too needed the help and advice we were given.

I also learnt a great deal from other patients and their partners. I was surprised that their support affected me so deeply. In the intensity and openness of that weekend a group of strangers had become intimate friends. I found I could safely share with them thoughts that I had previously only discussed with Paul. We were so close it was like talking to myself and he wasn't a patient, he had his own thoughts and anxieties. In the group I could talk about death without turning a friend white faced, and about trying to be positive without someone saying "you're so brave taking it like that". Only other patients really understand that being positive is a completely selfish attempt to stay sane. I was relieved to find that emotions and thoughts which seemed so eccentric and irrational had been experienced by others. Relatives too need this kind of reference.

I had discussed my thoughts and feelings, and the disease itself, with my friends and family many times and valued their support immensely. But their focus was, quite rightly, me, not the disease. Even so I was restrained by a fear that cancer would exclusively dominate our relationship and I didn't want that. Here I could finally let go and concentrate on having cancer but with the supportive backup I had previously only experienced with my family and friends.

By the end of Sunday afternoon both Paul and I were emotionally drained but full of the future. I had made two decisions. One was to continue writing about my experience. The second was to use every strength and skill I had to enable the practices and opportunities shown to us at the weekend made available to every cancer patient.

I had begun to realise that having cancer had given me some benefits but not enough to be able to feel there had been a meaning and a purpose to all that I had lost. Of course I couldn't say that if things had been different I would still have had those wonderfully happy times I had over the previous year. The gains, the additional time for family and friends, the lessening pressure at work, I could have had by having a child. I wanted more. The only way I could find it was if my experience could be used to make cancer more bearable for others. I felt I needed to move on.

A few days after the weekend I began to feel less dynamic. The way forward now felt less clear cut. I was conscious that the weekend had only scratched the surface. All the pain of the previous year that I had been too busy coping with to take time to understand was threatening to overwhelm me. The weekend had stimulated that process still further and I needed time and space to deal with the consequences. Writing became the necessary outlet. I curled up in a chair on three successive Fridays and scribbled most of what you have just read, or at least the narrative. Some of the more analytical bits came later. I can remember the feeling of relief, of a weight being lifted off me as I finished each section. Somehow writing it out lessened the emotional impact it had had before. By setting it out in some kind of order and imposing shape on it I had limited the experience and stopped it's power to endlessly reverberate.

By the time we went on our summer holiday I had finished the task and felt free to really relax into the holiday in a way I hadn't achieved since before the diagnosis. I had enjoyed the holidays we had had very much but hadn't in any of them had the same sense of careless freedom I now experienced. Partly it was also that the trip to Spain was a normal holiday; touring and camping, mixing sightseeing and climbing and relaxation in the haphazard way we had done in so many summers before.

We returned to an invitation to go on another weekend seminar. We hesitated a little, but in the end we both felt it was the right thing to do. I felt I had released the immediate tension in my writing but that the process wasn't finished yet. Somehow the weekend might help. I had nothing to lose and I wanted to stay involved. I was utterly convinced that the weekends were a wonderful and exciting development. I had felt what the last one had done for me and seen what it did for others. Maybe I could help develop them further. I had some contacts in the Department and several years training in drafting skills. They said they were going to write a book and they would need help in writing up their work to attract funding. The article I had written about the differences between my own hospital and the second opinion doctor had just been accepted for publication by the British Medical Journal which gave me the confidence to believe I had something to contribute.

Of course when I got there my intellectual detachment became increasingly irrelevant. Again I found the weekend was able to reach and resolve layers of anxiety that nothing else had touched. I was less nervous. Partly that was because I wasn't working on two levels this time; on the one hand trying to decide whether to change doctors, on the other following what was going on at the seminar. I was able to conquer my reluctance to express the anger I felt about certain aspects of my past treatment. In the heady context of that weekend the ghosts were finally laid. I can't really explain why, I just know it happened. Again we came away emotionally exhausted.

I felt completely supported for the first time. It was more than feeling totally understood, though that was part of it. My innermost thoughts had been listened to, more than that, responded to, by people who could expand on and build on that shared experience.

I've wondered whether I might have got to the same point by separately finding a doctor interested in advising me on what I could do to maintain my own health, a psychotherapist to help me work through my anxiety, and a support group to share my experiences. I doubt it very much. There is something very potent in putting all three together. It wasn't just support and a reference for my experience from other patients that I wanted, but the informed and directed support I got from the doctor and psychotherapist. Conversely, it wasn't just professional help and advice I needed but the way this was complemented by the sharing of experience with other patients and their partners.

It didn't matter that we were from different backgrounds and at different stages of treatment. We were united in what we were facing and what we had been through. I benefitted from seeing and talking to patients who had successfully been through years of treatment and who were finally in remission. Others who had only recently been diagnosed I think benefitted from seeing me so well after a year's treatment. All of us gained from the sense that our experience could inform and help others, sufferers and professionals. It gave meaning to what had seemed pointless pain.

Something was finally resolved in the course of the second weekend. It wasn't sudden but it was profound. The process began with the first weekend and continued long after the second. I wrote a few days later "The main feeling is one of release, of having lost a level of anxiety that nothing else has succeeded in reaching."

This feeling continued. I expanded the description a few months later:

I realise that this time I really have lost the mounting tension of the previous months. I was hardly an insomniac before but I've hardly had a single sleepless night since. I realise now how much the strain of living with constant uncertainty, and the knowledge I am probably incurable, has been taking out of me. I realise I have begun to understand and accept what has happened to me. It has given me a strength and energy that I have not had since before I became ill. Other people assume I am just finally recovering from the physical effects of chemotherapy, but there is more to it than that.

I appear to have coped and be coping extremely well. Rarely despairing, defiantly and determinedly positive. I sustained this attitude throughout almost a year of major surgery and intensive chemotherapy. It had little to do with maintaining appearances for others, I was fighting so hard I wouldn't admit negative feelings even to myself. But eventually I had to give way a little and come to terms with everything I had been too busy fighting to assimilate before. I'm still working things through, after all I'm still writing this. But it's not driven by anxiety any more, I'm writing because I find it interesting and exciting to explore what has happened in greater depth and to try and understand myself better.

I think others find it difficult to understand my need for introversion. After all I'm "well" now. Partly, I think, it is an understandable defensive reaction on their part. I'm well, lets ignore the implications please. Those closest to me are fully aware of the pain I still feel, despite being so "normal". I think those less close are beginning to suffer a little from battle fatigue: "Why do we have to go on making allowances, she's OK, let's just forget the whole thing". I still get occasional attacks of depression, but the "mean reds" never last more than an evening. My main need is to withdraw sometimes. I seem to have developed the courage to tell people so openly instead of just hiding myself away.

I'm not always as hopeful as I was. I can still be cheered and sometimes need to be by the possibility that technology will develop fast enough to cure me or that I shall be the rarity who has a spontaneous remission but by and large I have accepted that this disease will probably kill me. The funny thing is it doesn't seem to worry me so much as it did when the probabilities were much more in my favour. I guess I know it but don't really believe it. Right now it feels more remote than it did when I first heard the diagnosis. After all I'm physically fitter than I've ever been. You can only keep hitting a painful spot so often; after a while a merciful numbness takes over. When you experience some happy event that you'd thought you'd never see, and find yourself repeating it even, you begin to lose the fear that it will never happen again.

Trying to communicate how I feel isn't easy. Half the time I don't understand it either! Paul tries to understand but facing him with the possibility or probability that I might die hurts him so much. I realise I have coped with the possibility of the worst prognosis by facing it head on a long time before I really needed to, approaching it from every direction until it ceased to hurt. Paul copes by refusing to think of it until he has to and it doesn't help him if I force him to do it my way. I've only tried communicating how I feel to my closest friend. She too was hurt, shocked; turning my wording from probable to possible. My journey must be my own and no one else's.

It's not always easy. Sometimes I value what acceptance has given me, a joyful ability to be totally in the moment. Sometimes I am very conscious of what I have lost. I was recently promoted at work, the most important career step I will ever make even if I live to be a hundred! It was the culmination of seven years effort, but amidst all the congratulations and champagne I was a little miserable, very conscious too of all the career possibilities that were no longer open to me and probably never would be. There are times when I don't want to have the time to concentrate on what is important, to be lazy; I want to be unselfconscious and return to the days when I didn't have a free minute to call my own. I still have the occasional flash of resentment when I see my contemporaries able to carry on, as oblivious to their mortality as I was. It doesn't get out of hand, I'm quite capable of seeing, even at the worst times, the privileges those same contemporaries are denied.

47

Sometimes experiences still have resonances, birthdays usually do. I loathe New Year's Eve, all those cheery assumptions about where we shall all be five, ten, fifteen years hence. I like to think that these negative aspects do not predominate. Acceptance has by and large given me freedom. Completions and understandings have become not ends in themselves but a means of moving forward with greater strength and confidence than ever before. I am both more withdrawn when I need to be and at other times more extrovert than I have been for a long while. I again have the energy to reach out to new people and make new contacts without relying solely on those dearest to me. Perhaps I have finally learnt to simply be myself.

I have by no means given up. I've far too much still to do. I have just finally understood that it is possible to "fight" and "flow" simultaneously and without contradiction. Sometimes it is necessary to give way a little to find renewed strength. Sometimes I need to face pain directly. Only then can I let it go. This isn't a war which I shall win by surviving or lose by dying. Whatever happens I will eventually die. There isn't a battle but a series of skirmishes which I can choose to fight well or badly.

I had been so frightened of the acceptance that became my strength. I was scared it meant I was giving in and giving in I would make death happen. Looking back I began to see I wasn't always positive and yet that hadn't stopped me staying well. I didn't need to be perfect to survive. Being positive didn't mean being positive all the time.

CHAPTER 6

AN UNCERTAIN REPRIEVE

It's a good six months since I finished the last section. I lost interest in writing about past experience, I just wanted to get on with my life. I had been through a process of change, now it was over. Time to move on. Even when my article on doctors and communication was published in the *British Medical Journal* in December I couldn't get excited. It was all so long ago.

The first thing I did was to go home to New Zealand for Christmas again. A fairly last minute decision as usual. I was reluctant to book ahead in the face of my doctor's uncertainty as to how well I would be and the possibility of radiotherapy which would mean I couldn't go at all. In the end we agreed I was basically not very much worse than I had been when I stopped chemotherapy, so a decision on treatment was deferred. For the time being I would stick with hormones.

Home we went. Another instance of repeating one of those things I thought I would never see again. I relaxed and so did everyone else. This time we were treated more naturally and exposed to normal family conflicts and arguments. Not yet as participants, still observers. I hadn't until then realised how much everyone had been tiptoeing around on their best behaviour the previous year. We again basked in the sunshine, climbed mountains and renewed friendships.

We spent New Years Day climbing the Remarkables, a range of mountains aptly named. They rise sheer above a deep blue lake. It was very hot, still and clear. When we got to the top of the highest peak we turned round and round, drunkenly admiring the view. There were no clouds in any direction; a full circle of mountain peaks stretched to the horizon. I had never felt quite so on top of the world before. We slid down the thick snow which was still clinging to the bare rocks, skinny dipped in the ice cold lake below, and sunned ourselves dry. I felt it was an omen, a perfect day and a sign for the year ahead.

I remained an additional fortnight on my own after Paul returned. I enjoy spending a few days with my parents without constantly feeling like piggy in the middle, torn between them and Paul. I flew to Australia and had an exciting week with my brother seeing almost everything within a 200 mile radius of Adelaide. But it was probably too long a separation. I never really totally relaxed, missing Paul badly. And he found it very difficult coming back to a cold winter, work and no me. He got a lot of support from our closest friends but I think for both them and him there were times when my absence was a painful and poignant reminder of life without me.

All too soon I came back and had to make my own adjustment to winter and work. I had decided over the previous summer that bad prognosis or not I was getting fed up with marking time. Having a job without lots of short term demands, a considerative job I could do at my own pace, was boring. I needed a few challenges to respond to, though not too many. And I wanted to keep growing, to take on new responsibilities; to really get stuck into a demanding problem. Well the first step was to pass the promotion board I had been due to attend a couple of months after I was diagnosed the year before. I managed that before I went to New Zealand, but it was only when I came home that I had the opportunity to find a job at the higher level.

It wasn't easy. There was less flexibility at the new grade, no room to make allowances for the frail. I didn't feel that handicapped but I refused to hide the fact that I had cancer. It hadn't responded to treatment and was quite stable but I couldn't guarantee that problems wouldn't arise in the future. Still, I was willing to take on a real job with real responsibilities which would inevitably mean some pressures. I was willing to do all I could to cope with the inevitable unforseen emergencies which were part of life in the Department of Health but I was not in the business of proving what a wonderful and committed civil servant I was by working long hours as was expected of my peers. And I insisted on continuing to work only four days a week. I'd got used to having one day a week entirely to myself and I needed it to stay sane.

My prospective bosses divided into those who saw me as perfectly well and normal, and those who worried I might be at death's door and leave them in the lurch. The attitude of the former was "well the present incumbent is full time but I'm sure you could do it in four days". The others looked embarrasses and hastily interviewed alternative candidates. But I finally found a boss and a job which suited me; part time but intellectually challenging. It would involve working with the top of the office, and so getting the experience and exhilaration of being close to the centre I needed, but it was not a job with a lot of general political interest and hence a lot of unrewarding stress. At least that was the theory.

The thing I remember most vividly about those first few months back in England is being absolutely flat out. Always busy, dividing my time between trying to catch up with the friends I hadn't seen for two months and finding and starting a new job. I was happy to be so, totally absorbed in one thing after another; not wanting or needing introspection at this point. Partly this was due to my physical state. The latest check ups showed some improvement. I had a few more months at least. The end was not as imminent as I had thought.

50

Paul has got used to my ability for quick reversals, a habit formed long before I had cancer, but I think it was hard for the friends who had drawn so much closer to me over the previous eighteen months. One commented that she had been thinking how things had changed. How much time we had spent agonizing about treatments and doctors and where do we go from here. While she understood that I just didn't need that now it was darned difficult keeping up with me. "I think I know where you are and then I find you've moved the goal posts."

I was getting busier at work but I wanted to be able to use my experience of having cancer too in a more outwardly directed way. The only thing I could think of was to stay involved with the weekend seminars. But my role there was not clear, and I was becoming frustrated. I thought I had demonstrated my willingness to contribute in some writing I had done and discussions we had had before I left for New Zealand, but nothing seemed to come of it all.

So I went on another weekend in mid March. This time I didn't take Paul, I took my closest friend. I felt a bit sorry for her when I realised she was the only non spouse, but I shouldn't have underestimated either her or our relationship. There were some very depressed people on that weekend, and we seemed to be the closest couple there. Why did I go? My motives were mixed. First of all I wanted to take Pam. It was a promise I had made her a long time ago. What had happened on the weekends had deeply affected me but unlike everything else connected with my cancer was something I couldn't really share without her having been there too. And I hoped she might get something out of it for herself. As Paul had said the messages about personal needs and responsibilities and the techniques for improving one's quality of life were universal. It might be useful for me too. Previous weekends had uncovered layers of anxiety I hadn't known were there.

I also wanted to help carry the idea forward. Last September there had been talk of institutionalising the weekends, setting them up on a regular basis and using them to train other group leaders. I felt the excitement of development and intellectual debate and wanted to stay part of it.

Pam I think gained a lot from the weekend, and we grew closer as a result. I was able to give her the first three chapters of this to read. Much of the benefit had nothing to do with having cancer. In all the years of our friendship we had never made the opportunity to go away for a weekend together. No husbands, no children, just the two of us talking until two o'clock in the morning. It was like being a teenager again. Away from the world and all the other demands on us we talked about ourselves the whole weekend. Cancer wasn't a sensitive area for us, we had talked about it openly for so long, but we gained new insights. We talked over things at greater depth than had been possible when they happened. What I remember most is discussions about subjects we had rather backed away from before. Not cancer. Really sensitive issues; death and God. We reached a new intimacy.

One exercise moved me deeply. Many patients were very distressed on that weekend, haunted by unspoken fears of death. The psychotherapist decided to break through the impasse by asking us all to imagine our own death. Sudden and unaware, in a hospital bed or at home, alone or with family and friends, we all had our different images. When we examined them they turned out to be peaceful and reassuring, not frightening. One woman who had recently lost her husband described his death; at peace, loving, aware. We were all close to tears. I had kept sane the last few months with just such a fantasy. Now I had met someone who said it was real. It gave me new and unexpected strength.

I didn't find any unresolved anxieties. In fact I found it a bit difficult being there as a patient. I felt no need to talk about my emotions, though I was never stuck for words in general discussions and continued to be fascinated by other people's reactions.

Suddenly the months were racing past. I wrote in early June:

Cancer leaves me with a sense of urgency, an impatience, a feeling it must be done now because this may be all the time I have. A month or two seems an unbelievably long time not the short interval it is to everyone else. The weekends have given me a great deal, both in understanding what has happened and in stimulating an interest in describing it. I have continued following up my renewed interest in psychology with books and a few short courses. Now I want to move on but I don't know how.

It was not entirely plain sailing. There were doubts. A piece I wrote on 1 May seems to sum it up best.

I feel I should entitle this "Waiting for Godot" or rather I'm waiting, alone aware that Godot is coming. Cassandra perhaps? I don't know what I'm waiting for any more. This is beginning to feel like a phoney war. The last two checkups have shown that the one patch of tumour which can be felt is significantly smaller, though God knows what's happening to the rest.

It seems like all the uncertainty is coming back. I seem to have lost the almost serenity that acceptance of death gave me. I was convinced that this cancer would kill me a couple of years hence, not too close you understand, but real enough so I could see it. Was I really so calm? It was all a bit unreal, it wasn't going to happen in the next few months but conveniently far in the future. Now I don't know. The fantasies are coming back. A few more months of continuing to get better, then another laparoscopy and they tell me I'm in complete remission. I can visualise the details so clearly, it's like a familiar movie. I even have the characters rehearsing, I see the people who will be there.

Then what? Sometimes I see years more of uncertainty, and with it an opportunity to go further in the work I want to do to make cancer a more bearable disease, to have my revenge for what it has done to me. Sometimes a glowing future, years of a fulfilled and happy life. But there is always the shadow. The thought that it will all come tumbling down and end in premature death. Why is it harder now? I seemed able to accept it, and fight it, more easily when it seemed the only outcome. Now it's a possibility again, not a probability, it's become a threat, a source of anxiety. I don't understand myself. I don't have to make the best of it, it's not inevitable, and therefore I can't."

I was now in a fairly agitated state, as anxious as in the early days just after the diagnosis. Was this just a delayed reaction, anxiety about the fact cure was no longer possible? Perhaps I had reacted to that news a little too well the year before. That isn't how it seemed at the time. It was as if the reawakening of hope was more painful than living without it. "Despair I can live with it's the hope I can't bear".

I was frightened by my loss of serenity and upset by my inability to focus. What should I hope for and concentrate on? A month, a year, a lifetime? Part of me worried at every ache or cough. Part of me rejoiced in feeling well. But I was scared to trust how I felt. Cancer had taught me to mistrust my intuition.

Thoughts of my dying and death were giving way to fantasies of a miracle cure. I had been to the shrine of Our Lady of Walsingham the previous November. A tourist's curiosity had given way to reluctant awe in the face of all those names and candles. All that hope couldn't be completely futile or could it? There was nothing special about the uninspiring modern architecture. Bricks and a well. It could be any-where. Maybe God listened here. A prayer could do no harm. Maybe it had worked, maybe I was going to be the exception and prove all those dire predictions wrong. My more rational side told me I was being a romantic fool. The uncertainty bothered me. It wasn't something I could dismiss. I would just have to learn to live with it.

As ever I didn't think about having cancer all the time. But it was part of me, something that entered my conscious thoughts at least once a day. Not painfully, not at length, just there. It was a knowledge I couldn't dismiss. Of course it wasn't something I spoke about every day. In many areas of my life it wasn't something I spoke about at all. Having cancer was not something I routinely discussed with all my colleagues at work. If it came up in conversation I didn't hide it or avoid the subject, but nor did I dwell on it. For many of my colleagues I was just the same as always. Cancer was irrelevant to that sphere of my life and I was happy for it to remain so.

On the other hand I had changed. I had very clear ideas of what I wanted from work. I wanted a little allowance made for the fact that this cancer would probably kill me without having to broach the subject directly. In short I wanted to have my cake and eat it. There were a few problems. My clear ideas of the terms on which I was prepared to work became submerged in the pressure of coping with what was a far from quiet part time job. The subject for which I was responsible suddenly aroused a lot of high level political interest which no one had foreseen, least of all me. I began to feel overwhelmed.

I want to work at principal level. I get bored with too little responsibility, but I specified 28 hours a week because I want to work 28 hours. There is so much pressure to do more which I have coped with by doing more and more in the hours I am at work. It's been going on for two months now and I'm getting tired. It's not the temporary inevitable pressure of getting a new job off to a good start, it's now the norm with the expectation of even more work. I haven't had a Friday to myself for a while which probably doesn't help. I've had some sort of flu virus for a couple of weeks which I haven't been able to throw off, and it's left me feeling tired and debilitated. That worries me too. Maybe my immune system is beginning to suffer. But I console myself with the fact that Paul has had this bug just as long as I have.

Part of me wants to say "I have cancer, you're pressuring me too much, look my immune system is suffering, LAY OFF" to get some allowances made at work. I don't really want to use the cancer card though. I was happy (a top official) didn't know my circumstances and was treating me as "normal". I guess I forgot "normal" fast stream principals don't just do a good job, they are supposed to be willing to do a superwoman job. And whether I'm getting better or not I'm not in the superwoman stakes. I guess it was my own fault I got in this mess. I'm a proud person. I don't want to be pitied or patronised. I enjoyed the touchstone of someone who valued me for the work I did without knowing the circumstances. No danger of the "courage speech". But it seems to be encouraging expectations I can't meet. My having cancer just didn't arise. Trying to casually bring into the conversation the fact I work part time was hard enough, and that fell on deaf ears anyway. I may be open about my condition but I don't feel a need to bring it into the discussion all the time. I don't want to be a cancer bore.

Now there's the complication I might be getting better. Well that's for me to dream about. For work purposes I'm still stable and still fighting to keep that way for as long as possible. It's probably the truth anyway, but the possibility I might be wrong makes me feel guilty about my determination to press for more realistic expectations from my bosses. As I say I'm reluctant to play the "cancer card" but feel I have to now. I suppose it's hard for them, I mean those who aren't my closest friends to really understand. I look well, am physically well and now have been for a year; why should they make allowances? I don't wear my pain, my sense of loss, my uncertainty for all to see. Of course not. And then I expect them to make allowances for it. It's all unreal, so difficult sometimes.

As usual when quoting from my diary, in retrospect it all seems a storm in a teacup. Within a few weeks of writing that I had sorted myself out some supporting staff. My bosses had made some efforts to reduce the

54

pressure on me to more realistic levels too, tactfully emphasising my part time not my cancer status. I had time again for meditation, swimming and the occasional gossipy lunch. I continued to work full days, but not the hours of the previous months. I felt stretched but not stressed. That was more like it.

I needed the respite. My in-laws arrived from New Zealand for a few months. They did not plan to stay with us continuously but long enough for some additional demands on my rather thin resources.

I needed a little peace for another reason too. I had to cope with the death of a friend. Kathy had cancer, the same kind and stage of ovarian cancer I had. She had been diagnosed about the same time as me, we had suffered and failed to respond to virtually the same treatments. I hadn't known her long, but I felt I knew her well. We shared many of the same experiences, had similar views about doctors, other patients, alternative treatments and what we could do to help ourselves. We worried together about the feelings and reactions of family and friends. When I was first asked to meet her I had some qualms. I knew she had suffered more than I had and was more ill. But it was not something I felt I could refuse and of course when I met her all such doubts went by the board. I discovered she was funny and an instant friend and we met several more times. I still had no wish to join a support group, but talking with someone who would be a friend even if she didn't have cancer was different. It wasn't just about sharing experiences retrospec-tively anyway. It was also about having the same attitude and going in the same direction. I needed her and she needed me.

It wasn't easy towards the end. When her husband told me she was steadily getting worse and had been admitted to a hospice I had some doubts about going to see her. I remember walking in the door of the hospice feeling nervous and thinking "what the hell are you putting yourself through this for?" She was obviously very ill, but still herself. I felt she valued the fact I had come to see her, but it was a little awkward. She was clearly dying, but her language, probably for my sake, was all about getting a bit better, about the need to be positive. I didn't feel I knew her well enough to break through that, for she was obviously aware of her situation. It felt a little unreal. It was so public too. She was sharing a room with another patient. That seemed to be inappro-priate for death. It was too much like a hospital despite the friendly staff and the flowers and the constant cups of tea. I wanted my dying to be private, at home in my own bed.

I came away that evening feeling something important had happened. I didn't know what it was and couldn't describe it. I knew I wouldn't be going back. I had to let her go on from here without me. I felt strange and rather guilty going home on a fine spring evening. There was a beautiful bright red sunset. It was very still. Heavy clouds threatened rain and reflected a surreal light. That felt significant, right, but the ordinariness of the early evening traffic seemed inappropriate.

55

When I got the phone call telling me she had died I thought I took it very well. It wasn't unexpected after all. Then I put the phone down and started shaking. This was the first time I really had to face the reality of death. The shock continued. It wasn't just her death I was facing, it was my own. Death wasn't just a theoretical possibility or probability even. Sometimes it happened.

Her funeral wasn't for me a celebration of her life but a stark reminder of her death. I wasn't used to funerals. Kathy; gentle, loving, angry, vulnerable Kathy. She was gone and they put her body in that wooden box. Here. I could almost touch it. I couldn't cry. I couldn't feel.

In the weeks since I realise I have grown from the experience. I have learned that terminal illness and death aren't totally unendurable. The unknown has for me always been a source of anxiety. Now I know what hospices are like and how I want my end to be by seeing hers. I've lost a friend, and that will always be there but already the pain is fading. Towards the end it seemed she was suffering so much, and for such a long time. Now all I can think of is that it was only a few months ago that we were laughing over a pizza at the pretensions of hospice "lady bountifuls".

CHAPTER 7

TWO YEARS TO THE DAY

I wrote the last section nearly six months ago. It was a rare opportunity for reflection in that busy time. I was propped up in bed with
what my doctor thought was pneumonia. I knew it might be a malignant
pleural effusion. I wanted to write about those six months from the
perspective of being well.

Writing about the next few weeks is still painful, something I feel I
want to avoid. The waiting, the not knowing, stills feels the worst. On
Friday evening I went to my GP with increasing breathlessness, fever
and a nasty cough. We had been in Spain all that week, touring Granada
and Cordoba with Paul's parents. It was a lovely, lazy and adventurous
week which I refused to spoil by giving in to what I thought was a nasty
flu bug. I didn't feel particularly ill. I just had a bit of a fever sometimes,
but then it was nearly 30 degrees in the bright Spanish sun. It was silly,
I kept telling myself, to worry about a cough. I was just being neurotic.
Like a textbook cancer patient, over reacting to a bad cold. The
breathlessness only affected me when I did anything strenuous and after
all it was so hot and I did have a bit of a chest infection. But I was
shocked at how puffed I felt climbing the stairs to the plane home. And
I was so feverish I now felt dizzy and sick. I had to give in.

I knew a pleural effusion, fluid caught between the chest wall and the
lung, was a possible complication of my disease. My GP reassured me it
was unlikely to be that. I probably had a form of pneumonia. He
arranged for me to have an Xray at the local hospital on the Monday
and prescribed antibiotics in the meantime. A not too anxious weekend,
writing and coughing. I was feeling increasingly fragile and the breathlessness was getting worse though.

On Monday the Xray. I was now getting concerned; I could hardly walk
from the carpark to outpatients. Late that afternoon I had a phone call
asking me to return and see the consultant on Wednesday. Total panic.
That meant the Xray was abnormal.

I started to shake as I put down the phone. Restless I walked backwards
and forwards across the room. WHERE was Paul? At last he came
home. Understanding my fear he reminded me an abnormal Xray could
also mean pneumonia, that was why my doctor had sent me wasn't it.
Paul's parents arrived back from a day's shopping then. Paul's Mum
tried to convince me I must have a new kind of Asian flu. As I wrote in
my diary, "not well received". Poor thing, she meant well.

Should I ring my GP and get him to find out what was wrong before Wednesday? I didn't want to make a fuss and agonized instead. Writing didn't help any more. I couldn't bear to even try all my carefully practised relaxation techniques. I was restless and depressed at the same time. I couldn't do anything. Paul kept me sane by forcing me to watch Woody Allen. I slept badly. The next day's diary entry is "Totally unproductive. Watched TV, passed time."

I let my diary tell the next part of the story. It seems to convey what happened more immediately than any later recollection.

June 9 1988

I've mentally been composing this diary entry for months. "Two years to the day since the operation was done." I meant to write "if only I knew then that I'd be perfectly well, disease quite stable, coping with my first principal job, closer than ever to my family and friends. Even with a new "career" writing about cancer".

I nearly made it, but not quite.

I went to our local hospital. I had a two and a half hour wait to be told what I most dreaded. It was a pleural effusion. Worse to be told by a complete stranger to whom I had to quaveringly break the news that I had Stage 3 Ovarian cancer. She was shocked, so was I. And panicky. I had kept sane the previous few days by envisaging the scene as being told it was pneumonia. The stranger tried to be reassuring. She told me an effusion could be a symptom of a variety of illnesses and it still need not be malignant. I wasn't convinced, I could tell she wasn't seriously considering the other options any more. I insisted on going to my usual hospital to have it drained.

That night funnily enough I felt much saner and calmer than the night before. Having to just get on with it all made it more bearable. I cooked dinner and was able to be more sociable with Paul's parents. I talked to a doctor friend about work on the article he wanted me to do. That was possibly the most important contribution. I didn't mean to use him so but we did talk about what was wrong with me. He listened, and pointed out that sometimes fluid could also appear on the lung without it being caused by cancer. He didn't deny it could be for what I feared most, he simply pointed out it could be something else. He was more convincing than the other doctor. Result: hope.

I had rather a fitful night. Then at 9am today I reported to the chest clinic. Typical. On the top floor, no chairs. Little old ladies fighting for the receptionist's seat. Strange doctors again. I insisted on speaking to my usual doctor. Eventually I saw her towards noon. Another day in hospital waiting rooms. Same options, different interpretation. Her version : little chance it was anything else but a malignant effusion. I asked about the possibility my doctor friend had suggested. I was told, well there were a few rare syndromes which had this effect but they were so unlikely she wasn't even realistically considering them.

Result this time: total pessimism. Convinced I probably did have a malignant effusion. But somehow now I really am in the middle of this situation I seem to be able to cope. What was far worse was all that waiting. Hoping, focusing on the best outcome but knowing it might not happen, seems to require far more energy than simply making the best of a bad situation.

Rather a miserable afternoon, waiting again. Being mauled by student after registrar. And the tapping of the lung. Painful. Then nausea. Then aching. Now recovery and writing this. Maybe malignant, maybe not. Maybe the results tonight, maybe not. Maybe better to live with hope than knowledge? I just don't know any more. Maybe home tonight, maybe not. Whatever, a lengthy sojourn in hospital. Funnily enough it doesn't seem to matter. I can just go with it if I can escape as I have done for the last few hours with Madame Butterfly and my writing. Worked on the article for an hour. Felt totally sane. Not a wasted day after all!

11pm. They told me I could go home for the night. Paul gave up in disgust twenty minutes ago.

June 14 1988

Two years on. Again half dozing in my own bed in the afternoon sun. Peaceful, warm, the sound of birds in the trees outside. Just thankful to be home after the nightmare. Still physically shaky but beginning to see, at least psychologically, that there might be some light at the end of the tunnel. I keep thinking the same thoughts that kept me sane last time. I feel OK now, NOW is what counts. The number of tomorrows makes no difference to the quality of my life NOW.

The fact I got such devastating news two years to the day since the last time was bizarre, a word my doctor used. It was and is. Already I have lost the total devastation of Friday. Too shattered to write then so I'll never really capture that. I'm not sure I'd want to.

Paul waited with me all morning for the results of the lung tap. I knew they weren't going to be good by the time the registrar finally came at 3pm. I felt everyone was avoiding me because the news was bad. Yes it was a malignant effusion. Numbness. A new chest Xray had shown a lot more liquid was forming so it would need to be drained quickly. That's what my own doctor had recommended I was told. There were no real options now. I could start then and there or wait till I had seen her myself. Panic. Things were moving too fast. I said I would wait. The drain would need a pre-med and I wanted my wits about me.

After the pessimism of yesterday, I was half expecting my doctor to walk in with her retinue in tow and announce in a ringing tone that yes it was malignant and did I have any questions. After the last twenty four hours of waiting I would have ended our relationship there and then. I had more than enough. I was almost looking forward to a reason for exploding. I didn't get it. She completely floored me. Paul had pulled the curtains round my bed for a little privacy, to talk about the implications, and for me to be a little weepy. One nurse had already got her head bitten off for not respecting that but my doctor did. She put her head round the curtains and smiled a little ruefully. "If you feel up to it how about coming down to my office. It's a bit more private down there." We had our first ever audience sitting round a desk! She was very sympathetic and as gentle as she knew how. Information was volunteered. I got my first ever anatomy lesson about the functions of the lung. She described in detail exactly what they would try and do to stop the problem, and talked of patients she had known who had only had a single effusion and a long respite before progression elsewhere. It was quite alright if I wanted to "do the rounds", or she could speak to her colleagues about the options at a conference tomorrow. Discursive and sympathetic, she quite took the ground from under our feet. She would see me again after the weekend, once the drain was out.

She even seemed to understand something of what I felt, sharing my sense of helplessness. The unfair irony of fate having struck again two years to the day since the diagnosis. She told me that all her patients found the second time around the hardest. They all said what I felt, "I knew it would come but not so soon." And that was the essence of it. I had been so hopeful at the signs of remission at the previous checkups, only to have them so thoroughly dashed. That was what I cried for, the loss of recovery option. That fantasy I had been nursing over the last few months, the final laparoscopy that showed it had all gone away. Again we were back to an inevitable end, the question wasn't "whether" it was "how long".

Like the first time, the bad news was unexpected. Being unexpected made it seem even more devastating. Still she promised me "You'll pick up the pieces again. Whatever kept you going in the past will keep you going now. Keep up the meditation". (Huh! If it did me so much good then what did I suddenly do wrong.) Guilt is one of the things I remember most about that Friday. If I hadn't worked so hard, had meditated more, been more relaxed, all this wouldn't have happened. It was only a little niggle, not a serious preposition though. I knew I had been happy these last few months, busy but absorbed and fulfilled in what I was doing. Much happier than when I was trying so self con-sciously to get the most out of life. I knew that couldn't really be the reason. Still, it was daunting to find that all those changes in my general well being hadn't made that much difference to my predicted place in the statistical hierarchy.

I really was very upset about it all. Genuinely felt I just couldn't cope any more. Not all over again. There was a lighter side though. A funny side, unable to take myself seriously. I'd been working on the article on the weekends, in particular the bit on the definition of crisis. At one point on Friday night I was laughing and crying at the same time. Saying "my usual coping mechanisms just aren't working any more, I'm in crisis!"

Friday night was pretty gruesome. Morale was OK to start with. After seeing my doctor, determined to make the best of it. Inserting the drain was painful despite the local anaesthetic. I couldn't watch all that grinding away through my ribs and sent Paul away. Just as well, I couldn't stop the odd ouch and whimper.

Then a dozy night. Propped up on pillows in quite a lot of pain as they drained off another three litres as fast as they safely could. Just played a quiet meditation tape on automatic all night, dozing off occasionally. They gave me injections of pethidine to stop the pain. That made me nauseous, so I had injections to stop the sickness too but they weren't nearly so effective. The queasiness kept me awake. And the humiliation of having to use a bed pan. Still I had a lovely motherly nurse who seemed to understand how I felt. She was an agency stand in. I never saw her again. Perhaps I only dreamed her.

Saturday very boring but Paul stayed and I had a cheer up visit from Hedy. Still feeling pretty unwell. I don't remember doing much except dozing. Paul read a lot and did his marking. I had diarrhoea from the antibiotics. Humiliating enough to have a bed pan without that.

Saturday night. A chest xray was needed to establish whether drainage was complete. The kind taken in bed was not good enough. I was wheeled through the hospital in my bed, drain and all. I remember a surreal journey through the dark and quiet corridors.

Sunday. Again waiting for a doctor. Last night's Xray had shown the chest was pretty clear; time for the bleomycin to go in. Panic. More chemotherapy, though I knew this one wouldn't make me sick, just perhaps give me a short fever. A good sign, a sign of the necessary inflammation to bind the lungs to the chest wall.

After the chemotherapy went in, a respite. Drain disconnected, able to walk shakily to the loo. A break for my aching back and tail bones. Paul's parents came to see me. We had chosen that as the best time; no drain, colour in my cheeks. They were still very uncertain and a little awkward, forced to confront the reality of my illness. I began to feel feverish towards the end of the afternoon. Drain reinserted 5pm. Fluid poured out. Worrying. The doctor had said he didn't expect much. Little sleep.

Monday. The nightmare. Fluid continuing to pour out. Litres of it. I felt so ill. Temperature up and very nauseous. Paul stayed and fretted beside me most of the day. The promised doctors, always "on their way", never turned up till late in the afternoon. I was convinced that the

61

cancer had got out of hand. In a feverish haze I saw myself living only in hospital, connected to the drain for a few weeks until death. Paul was unable to reassure me. But he stayed. At one stage I saw what was happening as a peaceful vision of the future. Paul reading beside my bed, sometimes just holding my hand, as I dozed. This couldn't be my deathbed. This was what it would be like and I wasn't afraid. I didn't need to fight any more. I felt light, warm and sleepy. I could just give in.

The chest doctor finally came at 4pm. The fluid was only either a missed pocket from before or a reaction to the chemotherapy. Another Xray. My own doctor came. Finally someone on my side. In charge. Paracetamol NOW. "I know you're not in pain but it will make you feel better." Drain to be taken out, probably home tomorrow.

Late that night, the drain was taken out by an absolute cow of a junior. She was very rough, hurt me. Plaster ripped off painfully. She offered me no alternative but to "scrub off" the plaster remnants. I left it till the following morning. After a tearful half hour in the shower a nurse came to the rescue with solvent. Another wasted morning waiting for Xrays and results. Eventually released.

The absolute bliss of being home. Nausea starts to diminish at once. Psychologically so much better and stronger. Frustration at physical weakness. So pitiful. But strength slowly returning.

Saturday 18 June

Thursday, the joy of seeing my second opinion doctor. His usual optimistic self. He was able to reassure me by presenting the most hopeful interpretation. He wasn't surprised if a few cancer cells hadn't been floating round for some time kicked into action or reaction by a chest infection. If nothing more was happening in the pelvis it wasn't progression. Changing treatment not the result of desperation but because this form of hormone manipulation was being written about as getting very good results. Pieces very definitely being picked up.

Friday 21 July

Six weeks to the day since the nightmare, the day they told me. It seems so long ago. Thank God pain is a nightmare, to be forgotten when you wake up. I'm still connected to the event. I've still not got my usual stamina but I feel alive. Even going back as I do to the hospital is only a momentary qualm, a nasty taste in the mouth but no more. I remember feeling so depressed ten days ago when I thought I had to go through it all again, but it never happened. A false alarm, a nasty virus.

Even then I knew I could cope more easily. I would be better prepared, able to take decisions and make the most of it all. No tense unknowing. Perhaps too the security of my doctor's kindness, knowing I would be cared for. But it didn't happen. We're back to living from day to day, genuinely able to forget, to just not worry about tomorrow.

I was unable to write more for many months. Now, almost a year later I ask myself why the whole episode was so painful. I look at all the agonized screeds in my diary and wonder why it hurt so much. Maybe I can only face it because I have remained well and lost my fear of imminent death. I still know I cannot rely on the future but again I have learned to take at least the next few months for granted.

At the time the pain was very real. My body had let me down again. Not only had it let the cancer grow, it had let it do so stealthily, deceitfully. There weren't any clues. I had felt completely well. The only tumour that could be felt was growing smaller. Then suddenly I discovered that all along it was slowly, cunningly getting the better of me. And I found I was just as frightened as before.

Well perhaps almost as frightened. There were differences. Even when I was most upset, the writing and the reading I had done gave me at least a limited sense of detachment and understanding. It helped. It didn't diminish the pain but it limited it and gave it perspective. No endless reverberations of "why, why, why" this time. I had a structure into which I could fit my experience. And I knew I was not the only one to have felt like this. I wasn't going mad and it would get better. I knew.

The more detailed medical information helped too. More important still was the obviously concerned sympathy that went with it. I couldn't understand my doctor. What had brought out this sensitivity? She had shown an increasing warmth and willingness to be more informative over the previous months but nothing had prepared me for this. I felt as if she had read all that I had written about her and was determined to do better. Had she read what I had published in the BMJ I wondered? Part of me worried that she was being nice to me because she was sorry for me. It made me suspect that this was really the end.

I notice now how much it meant then to have a hopeful gloss on the medical details I was given. I never wanted to be mislead by unreal optimism, but then it was especially important that honesty be combined with a shred of hope I could cling to. Now I'm not so sure. I have discovered I need both my own doctor's realistic pessimism together with my second opinion's hopeful optimism. Both are honest, they just have different perspectives. If I had a fifty fifty chance one would describe it as a fifty per cent chance of getting better, the other a fifty per cent chance of getting worse. At times of crisis I only want the optimistic view, but when I've got used to the news I find I need the more realistic too.

Maybe I'm using one against the other. That way I know what the parameters of the possibilities are and I can choose my own interpretation and vary it according to my mood. I need them both. My own doctor is one of the very few people I have met who allows me to face the worst that might happen at each turning point. She not only allows me to face it but comes along with me, permitting me to explore it and prove it's not so terrible after all. The second points out that it might not happen, that there is always a more hopeful interpretation. I can't do without either of them but I'm not sure I could find both attitudes in one person.

I'm getting ahead of myself again. At the time I hoped, but didn't realistically expect, many more months of health. I quickly went back to work and found again a new depth of enjoyment in day to day pleasures. This time, fortunately, I lacked the painful self-conscious overtones. I seemed to have lost for good and all that sensation of wanting to hold a precious minute still for ever, frightened it would never come again. I quickly found I could lose myself, happily absorbed in everyday tasks, without thinking "what am I DOING?"

I wasn't totally relaxed though. I was determined to do my utmost to prevent the disease getting the better of me. As soon as I went back to work I decided I was fit enough to try swimming again. I was rather shocked. I didn't have the energy to do more than a few lengths. Gradually it got a little better. First two lengths without stopping. I was so proud of myself. Then three, then four. Within a few months I was back to a dozen lengths with only one stop for breath. The determination was beginning to take it's own toll though. Late one night Paul remarked that proving you're alive isn't the same thing as living. I understood.

We didn't often talk about the possibility of my death. It was too painful for us both, but occasionally I needed to know he understood my doubts. Sometimes his refusal to discuss his own fears made me feel he didn't care. Of course he did. But I needed to know that he understood. I was loved. He would miss me.

I was still very conscious that my prognosis wasn't good. I still felt a sense of urgency, a desperate need to make something constructive come out of my having cancer. I couldn't let it just be meaningless. There had to be a reason, something positive to come out of the premature ending of my life, our lives. At last it seemed I was finding it. Everything was fitting into place. I had been asked to work on an article about the weekends, and might get involved in writing a book. I wanted to make sure the project really succeeded in getting off the ground. If only I could make people who didn't have cancer understand how important it was to provide the kind of intensive support and opportunity for development we had found on the seminars. I knew I could write persuasively and I had had a lot of training in working up strategies. The civil service had given me skills I wanted to use for something more meaningful. I spent much time drafting the article and developing plans to expand the weekends. It would be necessary to involve other professionals.

I wrote an explanatory leaflet for doctors and patients. The doctor who had run the weekends wasn't terribly enthusiastic about my suggestions but my own doctor seemed to be taking a great interest in what I was doing. I decided that maybe it was time for me to change too. She had shown that underneath the sometimes brusque manner of the early days she really did care what happened to me. Maybe I should be more outgoing in return and trust her a little more. I decided to give her a draft of the explanatory leaflet and see whether she might consider using it to interest other patients in coming. I would also give her a copy of the draft article I had written the previous year about my feelings and experiences and how the weekends had helped, which might explain more articulately why they were so important to me.

I took the papers to my next consultation. My doctor was again friendly and informative, but a little more businesslike than before. The Xray was fine, the disease really did seem to have stabilised. "Did I have any more questions?" "No, that's it for this time" I smiled. "Good", she said. "There's something I want to talk to you about". What on earth?... "An article in the BMJ which I'm told you wrote under an assumed name". Oh. I was sitting on the edge of the examination couch ready to get dressed and go. I sat back and drew my knees up to my chest. Part of me wanted to just leave and never come back. Part of me had been waiting for this moment. Thank goodness Paul was there.

She was very hurt and very angry and yet it wasn't as difficult as it might have been. We discussed everything but the content of the article itself. Why I published it in my maiden name. How she had come to get a copy. She was very upset and, I felt, more emotional than I was. I felt a little frightened but totally in control. I wouldn't have chosen this. I hate confrontations. I go out of my way to avoid them. I always lost that kind of argument, especially with her. I sat there determined not to back down and say it was all a mistake. I didn't need to. We never discussed the real issues. I kept trying to explain how much I thought things had changed between us and how much I valued that change. I tried to tell her that I wasn't getting at her personally. It was the whole outpatient system which stopped me being assertive enough to ask for the information I needed. I wanted to explain I didn't expect her or any other doctor to be a mind reader. Setting up an outpatient system which allowed me to feel more like myself and less like a passive patient would allow me to overcome the vulnerability which the diagnosis had created. I managed to explain some of what I felt but not all. I was so shocked. Partly because I had befriended the person who told her about the article, another patient. Now I learned she had died. It was only a few weeks ago we had been laughing together. She had seemed well enough. Didn't anyone survive? Was pessimism always right?

I was unprepared too. I had written the article a year ago and it had been published more than six months before, just after we had left for New Zealand. It wasn't part of my life any more. My doctor had recently been so kind and generous to me. I wasn't expecting to have to deal with the issues directly. I thought I had found a way round the problem.

We ended the interview on a civilised, even friendly note as I asked for her help in sending a few more patients on the weekends. She was perfectly happy to co-operate.

I needed to get out of there. My voice was starting to quaver and my knees were shaking now. Shock was setting in. Paul and I left the hospital and walked round the park. It didn't take long for me to feel strong enough to go back to work. After all we had had a confrontation and I hadn't lost out this time. I was proud of myself. I hadn't cowered in the corner inarticulate and frustrated. Maybe I was changing too. I was glad things were out in the open at last. I had felt guilty and deceitful not knowing whether she knew what I had written. And I was small minded enough to feel a little vengeful satisfaction. Now she would know what it felt like. She had given me so much pain, not it was her turn. I knew I could heal some of the hurt by writing to her and explaining more clearly what I felt about the more positive aspects of her care for me. But I wasn't going to. It would serve her right.

Euphoria didn't last long. I spent the afternoon at work trying to concentrate on the proceedings of a very boring committee but I was just going through the motions. When I got home Paul was out for the evening. I sat on the bed in the twilight reading and rereading what I had written and reliving the interview over and over. I was uncertain now both about the conversation and about the article too. My diary notes: "I have begun to question whether my writing about cancer, and hence all that pain, does have any meaning. Perhaps it is just pointless and random after all". By the time Paul came in I was exhausted, but slept little.

The next day I had little time for reflection. I was genuinely busy, engrossed in my work. Then, that evening, I quietly began to write a letter.

Being as positive as I could about the non communication aspects of my care but carefully not budging or retracting one inch on my article. Why should I? I might make the same points in a different way today but that was how I felt about what had happened to me. I can afford to be generous. I think I have genuinely shocked as well as hurt her, made her see things she would prefer not to face. I cannot be dismissed as angry bereaved and irrational like (someone else who complained). Perhaps that is why she wants to put it down to personal animosity. But at least she is vulnerable enough to be hurt and upset. I have touched a raw nerve. The real test will be the next time I see her. She has reacted defensively before to new ideas but then accepted them without overt acknowledgement. We can only wait and see."

I felt the issue was pretty well resolved. Funnily enough I felt closer to her than ever. Her expression of hurt and anger had been a kind of compliment. She hadn't been cold or indifferent. She trusted me with how she felt. She had been human.

I posted the letter and left for our holiday determined not to think any more about the whole episode. The only thing that bothered me was an off hand aside. She had said at one stage : "The article is bad enough but I don't want to feature in the full length book". Oh dear. She couldn't know could she? It must be just a guess. Maybe she understood me better than I was giving her credit for.

It was now late in the summer but it seemed the effusion had finally settled down. We went on a camping holiday to France. I didn't feel it had to be anything special this time. We didn't have to consciously capture every minute. We could fritter time away, be bored and irritated if we felt like it. Our lack of self consciousness is reflected in the fact that we took far fewer photographs. We felt more relaxed, pottering about the Loire Valley. We went for walks when we felt like it, but I felt no urge to prove how healthy I was by climbing mountains in every direction.

Perhaps the diary entry a few days after we returned sums up the feeling best.

September 9

Nearly 34. Lying here in the garden, about to cook a celebration dinner for Pam and Graham. I feel like writing that entry planned for 10 June. "Who would have thought" .... There have been times over the last few months when this was very far from how I imagined my 34th birthday...

I seem to have fully recovered from the effusion, mentally anyway. I am at last able to forget about it. The reminders are involuntary rather than obsessive. I feel well. I forget about my disability until reminded by an odd ache. I remember swimming in France, totally relaxed, suddenly conscious I was running out of breath. I had momentarily forgotten I couldn't pound up and down the pool as before, length after length...

Today isn't a good day for my diary after all. I am just lazy, non intellectual. France was the break I needed. It took us both so long to unwind. Initial excitement, depression, irritation. Then real happiness and real enjoyment. I found so much energy. Real energy, mental creativity. Perhaps something new is beginning after all.

It wasn't just a fleeting impression. Something had finally changed. This time I had been through a traumatic experience and survived with the strength to go forward. To feel and yet understand. It was as if someone had hit me and I had let myself roll with the blow and now I was still moving without the need to stop and recover from my bruises. Having cancer could still hurt, deeply, but the detachment of writing was giving me a way of coping with the experience I had lacked before.

67

I felt I was developing courage at last. I was willing to explore the deeper waters of my own awareness because writing gave me a necessary detachment.

We came home from France with the strength to move into the future without taking it for granted. Paul began a three year part time degree course which would mean I would have to spend two evening a week on my own. We both felt it was time to move on. Even if there wasn't a long future we no longer needed to cling to each other just in case it was all the time we had together. I began to look forward too. We bought a piano, and to justify the cost Paul insisted I get some benefit. I started to learn music, something I had just never got around to before. It was one of those small gestures that later feels inordinately significant. It was the first long term project I had started since the diagnosis.

I quickly settled down at work. I took on additional responsibilities. It turned out (again!) to be not only an exacting area of work but a very pressured one, but with Fridays off I was broadly happy with the overall balance of my life. Although sometimes doubtful about the energy those extra work demands were taking there were compensations. I enjoyed finding out I could cope, more than cope, perform well in new tasks and previously untried skills. My career was doing better than it had ever done.

It wasn't all straightforward. One of the few diary entries that I made over the next few months records doubt.

AX died last week I learned today. He'd been diagnosed a year before me, and was always held out as an example. "A's had it for ages and he's OK". But he wasn't. He didn't make it. I knew he had had a recurrence. I didn't know it was terminal. Sometimes I feel the whole world is dying of cancer and I am the only one left. My turn will be next. Like ninepins all in a row. Why can't I know someone who survives? Someone who was really ill with it, not just had a little lump removed, neat and clean forever. Why just me?

I was sure the warm support I continued to get from my doctor was part of that new found security. The interview before I went on holiday seemed to have freed us both. She continued to go out of her way to be kind, carefully arranging appointments when she had time to talk to me. It got to the stage where I ended up feeling guilty that she was placing too many extra demands on herself by giving me so much time. I knew she couldn't possibly give as much attention as I demanded to all her patients. There simply weren't enough hours in the day. She would tell me to "just pop your things on while I write your notes" so I had these lengthy conversations fully dressed. When she was unexpectedly delayed her secretary was sent to explain and apologise to me. She was interested in what I was doing and had written about the weekends. What was more this was no idle curiosity. She was taking action to get her colleagues interested as well.

There was a relaxed friendliness, a warmth and trust between us that had been lacking before. I was partly glad she had found out about the article but had become rather guilty about how much I had hurt her. Even that seemed to be healing. Towards the end of the year I had a letter published criticising what I felt to be a patronising series of articles about how doctors should talk to cancer patients. I asked her whether she had seen it and hastened to add this time it was not intended to reflect anything about our relationship. "It's OK. I wasn't threatened this time." She grinned. "Much".

There are few diary entries over the next few months. Most of my life was happy and I didn't need to record what was happening, but there was another aspect which was so unhappy and so deeply hurtful that it wasn't recorded either. I finally had to come to terms with the fact that there was no role for me in developing the weekend seminars for cancer patients and their relatives. In retrospect it all seems so stupid, to get so worked up about something so trivial. A series of things happened which made it clear that the seminars would not continue and my help on either the weekends themselves or in writing about them was simply not important, neither valued nor required. Everything I had done so far seemed pointless. I was so hurt. Not just because of all the energy I had spent on planning and writing over the previous year but because of what I felt I had potentially lost.

December 11

It's all over. Part of me is still hurting. All the expectations, all the dreams. That's all they were. I realise I've been searching for a way of avoiding the truth I thought I had found last year. The meaning of my life has to be found in what I make of each and every day, my interactions with the people who are close to me. I had been building up the weekends, and my role in them, to something more than they were. Developing them, putting them on a secure basis, was going to be my life's work, my contribution, my revenge for what cancer had done to me.

Those dreams had been such a big part of my life, perhaps too big a part. For eighteen months they had been my lifeline, ever since I had been on the first seminar. Then I discovered they had all been an illusion. I knew it was mostly my own fault for losing realistic perspective but that awareness didn't help. There had been many signs over the previous months that my vision wasn't shared by everyone involved but I had chosen to ignore them. I had dismissed the warnings I didn't want to hear and clung to frequently reiterated commitments.

Soured personal relationships were involved too. The break was not made easily or cleanly.

Looking back I see I'm exaggerating. My reactions now seem totally out of proportion to the events. That was not how it felt at the time. It is difficult to give pain a value. Impossible to see it objectively. At the time losing the work on the weekends hurt more than having cancer. Perhaps that is why I cannot write about it. I am close to it still.

CHAPTER 8

PATTERNS REPEAT

Down but not out. Looking back the pattern was predictable. Why do I always react with defiance? The harder I fall the more I defy my aggressor. Telling me I can't do something is the one sure way to get me to do it, or I convince myself I never wanted it anyway. Paul has known that for years, why do I never learn?

It was just before Christmas. One Friday afternoon I allowed myself. I walked absentmindedly round Bromley attempting some last minute Christmas shopping. I needed to escape the phone and get out of the house. I cursed myself for being so unreasonably, so irrationally close to tears.

Then I plunged into a busy round of Christmas socialising, exhausting country walks and long neglected house renovation. It hadn't been all wonderful. There had been tension too. No need to spend all that energy on the weekends. I had time for more general reading, for music, for friends. I had no difficulty making the most of it. There are no diary entries for this period. I was much too busy getting on with life. I had no wish to be introspective.

Searching for significances again I interpreted the whole episode as a necessary and salutary lesson. There I had been last year thinking I had learned that life was for living, that immortality was contained in the memories of friends and family and shared experience. All the time I had been deluding myself and living in the future, looking beyond my immediate circle.

I couldn't just start off back where I had been the year before though. There was still a need to move forwards and outwards which wouldn't be suppressed. I wasn't the same person I had been the previous year. The resolution of my anxiety about dying, however fragile, had given me the desire and the energy to move into the future. I couldn't go back, I didn't want to go back, to that painful selfconscious awareness I had had before. I had to keep writing.

I didn't need the weekends as a vehicle anyway. I had my own views. I could write my own articles. There were a few drafts around, short pieces which had started out as a means of sorting through ideas about the experience of living with cancer. I worked on them over the Christmas holiday, and then tried them on a few friends. Encouraged by their support I sent the one I felt was the most finished off to the

71

Guardian. For the next fortnight I rushed for the post each day but there was no reply.

Defiance left me feeling a little tired. I felt fragile, out of touch with my centre. Perhaps there were just too many distractions. Work was particularly busy as my "quiet" part time job again began to get out of hand. Physically I didn't feel quite as energetic as I had a few months back. There were so many reasons to choose from; side effects of the new drug regime, the pressure at work, long suppressed fatigue finally catching up with me. I knew too it could mean that my cancer was getting worse. And so did my doctor. She ordered tests. Blood tests were all normal. Then a CAT scan. I tried to be positive. Might as well make use of one of the marvels of modern science.

The reality was something of a shock. Having to drink pints of radio opaque liquid. Then having to walk the long corridors from Xray reception to the scanner with a full bladder and a pert radiographer who asked repeatedly whether I was sure I wasn't pregnant. For once I didn't feel like being the charming patient. I told her that it was a pretty tactless question given the circumstances. She blushed and disappeared. A sparkling new room. It seemed much too large for the scanner, a small bed that slid through a steel tunnel. Claustrophobia was the least ordeal. First the enema. Hell. No one had warned me about this. At least he put a screen over the viewing window. But I still felt so exposed, lying on a narrow bed in that large room. It wasn't painful but it was uncomfortable. The enema made my bladder feel fuller than ever. The sensation got worse while I lay there for the next half hour as the machine whirred up and down. When it was over I wondered whether I could make the few yards to the toilet. I did. Just. Painful release. Shakily I returned to work and tried to put the whole episode out of my mind for the next week.

I was weary. Sick of hospitals, sick of being a patient. I had really forgotten what it felt like. Nearly two years since chemotherapy had ended, six months since the effusion. I avoided hospitals as much as I could. I didn't feel like a patient, though an unexpected whiff of that unmistakeable odour of cooked cabbage and disinfectant, or the unexpected sight of a drip stand, could still bring me up sharply.

The news was good though. The CAT scan didn't show the cancer in my abdomen my doctor had been more than half expecting. All it showed was "an admirably full bladder". I knew it didn't mean the disease wasn't there, just that it didn't show up on the scan. I refused to dwell on the negative. I felt reprieved, given a gift. I realised how fearful the loss of the weekend seminars had made me, frightened I would die before I could make anything of this experience. I felt it was a sign, an opportunity, at least another few months.

Relief was followed by frustration. I continued to review and comment on BACUP publications, but I felt I didn't add anything other contributors couldn't. I turned my attention to the hospital. Fed up with delays and callous treatment I wrote to the general manager chivvying him to do something about setting up a more humane outpatients system. I concentrated on the Xray department where I wasn't treated with the same consideration I now got in radiotherapy. Even that department wasn't above criticism. Though I now received special treatment I wasn't sure much had changed. There were still the same long unexplained waits for others. I overheard a receptionist saying sharply "I know it's a new lump but the doctor says you don't need to come in. It can wait till your next appointment". I felt for the poor soul on the other end of the telephone. So nervous at having rung the hospital I knew they wouldn't have the courage to protest.

There were some changes though. I saw patients with that dazed look of the newly diagnosed coming out of examination rooms with BACUP booklets clutched in their hands. I overheard a nurse saying to a patient going into a consultation "Would you like to bring your husband in with you?" Maybe a bit of constructive criticism from patients could do some good. I was pretty furious about the treatment I had just received in Xray anyway, and it would make me feel better to complain.

It wasn't enough. I needed a better way of acknowledging that having cancer was an important part of me. I needed to able to discuss what it meant, not just to share my emotions and thoughts with my immediate friends and family but interact on a more intellectual level. I wanted feedback and stimulation. Without the weekends I went back to my old friends. Books. I discovered texts for professionals caring for cancer patients which described some of what I was going through. Some scenarios were familiar to me, others made me say no, it's not been quite like that. It was helpful but not enough. I was too isolated. I wanted discussion, people.

Out of the blue opportunity came. My frustration that the weekends had finished came out in conversation with my doctor. She hesitated a little. "It's only just occurred to me" she said. "I haven't thought it through but maybe you'd like to consider participating in a teaching seminar I'm setting up for medical students on breaking bad news." It would involve taking a small group with a partner, a Macmillan nurse, to talk through and develop the themes in an introductory video. She seemed a little embarrassed, hesitant, not wishing to pressure me into accepting because she had asked. She advised me to go away and think about it.

I didn't need to. I'd love to do it. It was the outlet I needed and I couldn't help see it as an acknowledgement that my criticism the previous year had hit home. The last barriers between us were coming down.

Suddenly it was a turning point. A few days later I got a letter from the editor of the women's page at the Guardian. My article had been "mislaid" (really?) but she would be pleased to publish it. It would appear "as soon as possible" whatever that meant. I wondered whether it was a good idea after all. Did I really want to make public such intimate thoughts on living and dying? Too late.

I began to think about another trip home to New Zealand. My doctor shrugged her shoulders and grinned: "No reason to suppose you won't be as well as you are now". Then the seminar. It went well. I think the students benefitted. It wasn't that I could tell them anything different to what they could learn from a good textbook on communication skills but I could illustrate with examples from my own experience and I think the lesson had more impact coming from a patient. It was rather a new experience for them to come across a body which answered back. It had it's funny moments. At the end each group had to report back on their discussions. I had talked about the importance of doctors being human, of empathy, of how defensive mechanisms like brusqueness emphasised a patient's lonely helplessness, of how the words "I'm sorry" helped. It got reported back as the importance of doctors being apologetic and I wondered whether I had done them any good at all. I certainly gained from talking to the students, from listening to their point of view and from having to formulate my ideas coherently. Frustrated that I hadn't explained exactly how I felt, I finished off a second article on why it was important to know where I stood, however bad the diagnosis or prognosis, and sent it off to the British Medical Journal. It was accepted very quickly.

The Guardian piece was published soon after. I held my breath for days. It was the reaction of my colleagues at work I was most concerned about. I needn't have been. Few mentioned it. I was touched by those who did though, overcoming their awkwardness to talk to me. In the weeks that followed I also received letters from other patients in whom it had struck a chord.

I was finding writing rather a lonely outlet. I had finally accepted the weekends were finished and I wanted to explore the possibility of taking them forward in another direction. The knew the kind of support and gathering together of information they provided made such a difference but a weekend at a country hotel wasn't an essential part of the package. Maybe I could work with some of the friends I had made there, and the staff at my own hospital, to set up a group closer to home. We could start with a monthly support group. Surely that wouldn't be too much to ask? I still had a vision of much more. If centres like the Royal Marsden were able to set up a whole network of support services, ranging from dieticians and occupational therapists to relaxation lessons and art and music therapy, surely other hospitals could be encouraged to broaden their concept of treatment to include more care and psychological support. My doctor seemed very receptive and we talked about others who might be involved and the setting up of an introductory meeting.

All this would have to wait till later in the summer. First I would be going home to New Zealand. It was a trip I had promised myself the year before, a goal to aim for as I recovered from the effusion. Now, more quickly than I had thought possible, it was spring and we had to book quickly. I wanted to see my family but this time too both Paul and I wanted the opportunity to have a holiday on our own. We had always loved exploring new places and regretted that we hadn't been able to stop at the exotic destinations we had flown over on our previous two trips. This time we planned our six weeks so that we would have half with our families in New Zealand and half exploring the Far East and Australia.

Death suddenly seemed far away. I had cheated it more than once. I felt it was time to stop worrying and simply get on with my life. It is the little things I remember. I went to the dentist for the first time in three years. I reprimanded a four year old for wrecking my house. His mother beamed at me. "It's wonderful to hear you concerned about the house. It seemed like you didn't care before. I don't know. It's just that you really seem to be acting like a person with a future all of a sudden".

Of course there were still some doubts. But they were fairly subdued. Melancholy rather than despairing, accepting rather than angry in tone. Death was far in the future again.

MAY 19 1989

Why is today so significant? I've been searching for reasons. Why this vulnerability, this fragility today. A year and a day after Kathy's funeral. Reading N's book? Just a heavy week? A few days to the next check up? Or knowing the holiday looms and I so want to go?

This evening in the garden. Dinner by candlelight and Paul with his pipe. Talking in the warm darkness. It's something that will linger as more significant than it seemed at the time.

This afternoon I lay in the garden. I intended to work, to read a psychology text. Write this. But I didn't. I lay and admired the roses and went to sleep. I thought back the three years to convalescence, the pain and the joy the garden gave me then. The joy because I thought it was about to end forever. The pain because of all the time I'd "wasted" preparing something I would never see. What was a bare trellis then is today covered with clematis and roses. The grape vine we planted the weekend I came out of hospital covers the fence.

When I die I will be immortal. I will live on in the people I love and who love me. They will take a little of me with them. My thoughts will survive in my writing. My experience as a patient will survive as long as my doctor practices. A little of me will live in the garden on warm summer days. A little bit of a ghost. A friendly, quiet one. Perhaps a spirit. A spirit of happiness. I do feel so happy. Part of me asks, does that mean it won't last? Part of me says it is why I am well and will continue to be well. My trouble is I am too imaginative. I can see the miraculous future and death. Both. I don't know which one will happen.

Maybe all this is just because it's the first heat of summer. It brings back memories, doubts. Last summer. The summer of 86. Maybe it's because I'm well. The angst of uncertainty. I should know by now that's always the hardest.

I feel so guilty faltering like this. I am well, I've been perfectly well for more than a year. All in all the disease has changed or grown very little in the last three years. Few patients have that kind of reprieve. Why then the anxiety? It's not the same as I felt last year when things were going well and I felt I had more to lose. I described it tonight to Paul as feeling more like a gambler whose luck must be running out. I'm tossing a coin and so far it's always come up heads, but the chances of that get smaller every time it happens. Every month that passes, every year, I both feel very fortunate and very frightened. Out on a limb. I am defying the statistics but the chances seem to be stacked more heavily against me the longer I go on.

Shadows were a small part of my life though. I was busy; at work, writing, with friends, planning our trip around the world. I was very conscious it was early summer again, and ready to see significance in the recurring anniversaries. June 9 and 10 again loomed large but I was determined they would have very different resonances. And they did.

They were fine clear sunny days. On the Friday I arranged to have my hair cut. Short and stylish. It was a final recognition of the fact that it would never grow back as thick and straight as it was before I had chemotherapy. I quailed a little when I first saw the result, then decided I liked it. A new, more lively image. Then an afternoon treat, a visit to an old friend and her new baby. No Friday chores or obligations. Saturday evening was spent at a friend's 40th birthday party. I was in a mood to celebrate. I kicked off my shoes and danced till the early hours to the records I hadn't heard for years. It wasn't just nostalgia. Part of me still was that idealistic young student. I felt completely carefree. Dancing mentally as well as physically.

On the Monday a friend congratulated me on my piece in the *British Medical Journal*. Not only had my personal view on the value of knowing one's diagnosis and prognosis been published, so too had a letter outlining my views on the importance of broadening the concept of cancer treatment to include more in the way of care. What wonderful timing! Now I was really high. Maybe God was merciful after all. This had to be more than coincidence. I remembered a graph of the mortality rate for ovarian cancer I had seen years ago. A sharp downward curve for the first three years after diagnosis then a virtual straight line. I had passed that magic point and nothing would stop me now.

The next few weeks were an intense bustle as we finished off at work, made last minute preparations for our holiday and said goodbye to all our friends. Our holiday was going to be both exciting in itself and a new beginning. Taking off for New Zealand felt like an apt metaphor for the years ahead.

The trip more than fulfilled our expectations. Cancer was pushed aside. There was so much to see and do, it absorbed all my attention. We gazed open mouthed at the gilded temples of Bangkok, were moved by the poverty and dignity of the Thai people. I remember orange clad monks walking the deserted streets barefoot in the early morning rain. I remember the bombardment of the senses in Queensland. Rainforests, crocodiles, coral gardens, bright tropical fish. Sunsets, clear sunlit water, long white beaches and coconuts. Family and friends in New Zealand. Never having enough time to see everyone and do everything. Catching up with an old schoolfriend in a whirlwind tour of Sydney. A peaceful week with my brother in South Australia. Talking round the fire. Rain on the iron roof, kangaroos and koalas outside the door. A few days in Singapore. On our own again. So much to see.

We arrived home full of the future. I was looking forward to going back to work. My job had been redefined while I had been away. More responsibilities, a new boss, so much to be sorted out. Enjoyable as the holiday had been I was impatient to get back to real life. I was impressed by all the work both my brother and my sister had managed to do on their Victorian houses since I had seen them last. It was about time I settled down too. Less of this dreamy meditation about the meaning of life and death and a little more practicality was in order. I was making plans years ahead, my brother doing a year's secondment over here, us living and working in Australia for a year. I was restless. Time to really live and forget about cancer.

Before I was diagnosed I assumed that if I ever learned I had only a short time to live I'd give up my everyday life and do all the things I meant to do one day and never got round to. In reality I've found the reverse and it's the everyday routine that seems the most precious. Projects are fun and life enhancing but ultimately not that important.

CHAPTER 9

AN END OF SORTS

The dream lasted till the night we came home. In the bath that night I fingered the scar where the effusion had been drained. It was a familiar ritual, it had been getting lumpy for months. I knew that it might mean a little tumour was growing there. My heart skipped. It had moved. And grown. There was quite a large lump underneath my finger. Further up. In my armpit. Oh God. It's not moved. It's a new lump.

On the Monday morning I telephoned my doctor. She gave up her lunch to see me. She was kind, human, sharing my distress.

It might be progression it might not. I would need Xrays, mammograms, then surgery. There would be no real answers until the lumps had been biopsied. All the uncertainties were back again and it was just as hard as it had ever been. Harder. I had been well for more than a year. I had learned to take it for granted. I didn't know how to be a patient any more. That was no longer a central feature of my life. I was too busy. I wanted to get embroiled in all the usual crises I had just discovered on returning to work. I didn't want to relinquish that carefree sense of time I had found on holiday. This was all wrong. I wasn't ready. It felt like a very nasty black joke. And I didn't have a sense of humour any more.

I lasted a few days, going through the motions. Then it all got too much and we again escaped to walk the cliff tops at Seven Sisters. I mulled through the obvious parallels. Three years since that walk the day after I learned chemotherapy had failed. Remember what they said then. I had had one reprieve from a dire prognosis, maybe I'd be walking the same cliff tops three, five, ten, twenty years hence. Optimism alternated with despair.

September 24

Again a lazy Sunday afternoon in the garden. I have been here so many times before. But there is no sun today, just the chill mistiness of autumn. The summer is over. I am resting from the activity of the last few days. Has the time come at last to face the pain? To look it straight in the eye and recognise it as mine? I know the cycle too well. The initial shock and the quick rebound. Determined not to give in. It's hurt enough. Time to recover. Silly to waste whatever time is left. Energetic activity. Distraction. Intense joy in deliberate treats. Then tiredness, depression. It can't be sustained. All this within the space of a weekend.

Thursday I reached end of tether point. For three long weeks I had been maintaining hope across the whole spectrum from a completely new cancer to a benign lump "just like anybody else". Then that silly week of cancelled appointments and waiting from day to day. I couldn't stand any more. I telephoned from work. My mistake. An awful way to get bad news. Still no date for surgery but now I know it seems pretty certain there has been some progression. A new cancer from the effusion last year. Only small lumps. But I can't keep a sense of proportion. I didn't expect it to hurt so much. Part of me has known that I received a sentence of doom three years ago when I didn't respond to the first chemotherapy. Part of me never accepted it. Just like last year. All the signs had been indicating the disease was getting better. The fantasies of cure never came back but I felt I was living with a long and indefinite future. I was making assumptions, plans for at least a few years hence.

I feel I have been reined in. Sharply. I have lost that sense of carelessness I had on holiday. I feel cheated. I had really let go, changed my focus. I had had no major hiccup for more than a year, and on holiday I had finally accepted that. I had believed in that neat symmetry, a three year trial and a new beginning. Now I see it as an illusion, a trick of my imagination. I feel so disappointed.

The future is short term again. I so resent that. I am reluctant to give up the long term. It is so limiting. As yet it carried no joy. I don't want to hold the moment. I resent I can't let it go. I have so enjoyed the last few months. Unselfconscious. Not circumscribed within the limits of cancer. Free. Being alive isn't that joyful fragile walking on eggshells. It's on the other side. Oblivious. But not totally unaware. Knowledge I won't give up. I don't want denial but forgetfulness.

Now I am forced to confront the fact that the cancer is slowly progressing. Nothing has stopped it, my doctor suggests that treatment never even slowed it down. It's slow development was just biology, luck or me. It's like the tide coming up the beach. It may ebb and flow a little but gradually it comes further and further up. One day it will get so far it will kill me.

Why does it hurt so much? I knew it would come ages ago. But it does hurt. It's not so easy to defy when you can feel a lump gradually getting bigger. It really is there. Perhaps there's a part deep inside that still thinks it's all a dreadful mistake. That this can't happen to ME. Now I can feel it. Just little lumps. They don't hurt. If no one told me they were cancer they wouldn't concern me. How could my own body, part of myself, do this to me? My body has never really refused me before. If I wanted to do it I could. Now I can't. Something alien is taking over. This is too much. I know that isn't true. Why does it hurt so?

Why do I feel I've had enough. Even as I write I know I've been here before. It's just a matter of waiting out the storm. But I still don't know how to handle it. Do I go out defiant? Saying well I'm not going to waste the time being miserable. Creating a full social life, busy at work, filling in the spaces with spring cleaning, house renovation, swimming and squash. Well I've done a bit of that these last few days. Made an effort to be with people I don't know well enough to want to talk about what is happening. Enjoyed the parts of my life which have nothing to do with cancer. Or do I withdraw, let myself sit in quiet depression. Write. Refuse to go to work. Will it help? I don't know. Does it really help to give in? I just don't know. Yet after giving in a little I know I feel better. I can be busy, active and absorbed. Is it recovery or reaction though? Is it just that old determination not to give in to pain?

All I know is it hurts. Being prepared for this intellectually doesn't help when you're living through it. It's one thing to know something will happen, quite another when it's happening now. Nothing prepares you for the shock.

It's not easier, it's harder having been there before, knowing there are fewer options now. I've had my share of luck. Now it's run out and there's no more. I feel like Faust. I've had the time I bargained for.

I'm not starting with a blank slate any more. I know how this hurts. So I fight. I go round telling myself the worst may not happen. Then it does and it hurts more than ever. I know what I'm losing. Maybe I recover more quickly but I still hurt.

The future frightens me. I don't think there is one. My doctor suggests that maybe the time has come to stop active treatment "for a time" but I think that means forever. She is weary, so am I. She is trying to be positive. Saying that I have probably stayed reasonably well in spite of rather than because of the treatment. Still lack of a positive response means it has had no effect. Stability or slight progression isn't a response to treatment. She makes it sound so logical but I am still afraid. The cancer grew fast and out of control before treatment. With treatment it has hardly grown at all. I don't know if I feel strong enough to handle unarmed combat. Me versus the cancer. Whatever I could do hasn't stopped it so far. Anyway she said the reason for going on hormones was to slow the cancer down. How does she know it isn't working then?

At least there is no distance between us now it really matters. No more standing by the door with arms folded. For the first time she sat on the bed, her arms around me. Suddenly tears don't matter any more.

Another round of questions, tension, unknowing, second opinions. I've had enough. Distractions don't work. I must sit it out. Write. Read. Needless to say one of my coping texts. An apt title: "Facing Death".

October 4

I should be prepared for progression, I have known for a long time that cure was pretty well impossible. I still can't resist the "pretty well". At the back of my mind there was still some part of me that never accepted it. And why should I? I don't want to. Why should I give up my dream, my hope of cure? If I give it up then I'm a pessimist not a realist. Waiting for the worst to happen, not looking to the best. What a narrow, limited way of looking at the world. Let the bad news take me by surprise, not the good.

It's not easier as time goes on though. It's harder. I know but I can't accept. I've proved all the predictions wrong so far. I've outlived the original prognosis. Maybe it will all get better after all? Maybe it is just a terrible mistake? No, I can't sustain that any more. It's there. I can touch it with my finger.

October 6

I write this in the midst of uncertainty. In bed recovering from the surgery. I know the biopsy results are unlikely to show anything else but that the disease has progressed. However ridiculous it is hard to give up all hope until the reality is there. Even though it is expected it will still hurt. It always does. We shall start another round of debates and decisions. Treatment or no treatment, hormones or chemotherapy. I know I will learn to cope with yet another door having closed. Yet another shrinking of the horizon. And there will be times when I am conscious of it and times when I am busy enjoying friends, family, or work. There is so much to look forward to. Three weekends away with friends over the next month. More writing and speaking about my experience of cancer to be done. A support group to organise. Problems in the Department to sort out. I will be busy, happy, absorbed.

I have learnt to see patterns. I know that trauma, uncertainty and anxiety are balanced by my enhanced enjoyment of life. Without the one I wouldn't have the other. I can understand the necessity of death. Knowing I will die has given life an urgency and meaning my assumption of immortality never had. Cancer is almost worth the conscious appreciation of life I have gained. I have not only had more time for my family and friends I have also grown much closer to them. The knowledge that there might not be much more time has made us all less reserved. That seems to have affected all my relationships. I am at last learning to overcome my shyness. I have had time to sort out my priorities in life and to act on them as well. Perfect days, hours and moments are still possible. Pain is finite however unending it seems at the time.

Mind you I distrust myself here. I don't want this to sound like some religious tract. I am no fan of martyrdom. I can accept what has happened as a little shadow to enhance the light only if I survive to a ripe old age. I am happy to have learned a lesson provided I am let out of school at the end. Having cancer has had it's positive aspects but unless I start getting better they are not enough. There's a whole world out there and I have explored only a small part. I have had the opportunity to discover talents I didn't know I had. I want time to develop them. I have found a new intimacy with friends and family, but I want it to be a beginning and not an end.

I still feel cheated. I am still resentful. Not against anyone in particular, but because it was me that was singled out. I rarely let myself think of the life that might have been these days. It feels unreal, a life that would have belonged to someone else. Paul feels it more strongly, he has gained less. He talks of life since the diagnosis, whatever the gains, as the "also ran" life. I know what he means. I feel if only I had more time I could make it equal what might have been. If only I had more time. Time I could rely on.

I am a little frightened as I look forward. Cancer has taken much from my life but not everything. I am fortunate in that it has not prevented me from being essentially myself. It hasn't altered my appearance very much; more importantly, it hasn't stopped me working. I have even had opportunities to develop my skills in new directions because of the cancer. Perhaps that is why the worse nightmare for me is that it will affect my brain. I see now it doesn't need to get that far. I can see it stopping me working, for the first time really challenging my identity, and I am a little frightened. I'm not sure I will be able to cope with that. I fear not being able to be myself, I fear being ill for a long period, more than I fear pain or death itself.

FRIDAY OCTOBER 27

It is an end of sorts. After two months of hell. Eight weeks to the day when I came home and felt the new lump. At last I know roughly where I stand. All that uncertainty has been the hardest.

The tumour under the scar was malignant. I knew that before my doctor told me. She knows how it hurts. It makes such a difference knowing she understands, that she really does care. We talked about the options. I realise it must be difficult for her to have to talk so frankly. It's difficult to keep a comfortable distance when you have to talk as directly as I demand. She is used to being busy, practical, in control. I have no social problems for her to sort out, even medicine cannot help me much and I won't let her take over. I offer no easy distractions. I begin to realise why she needs such substantial defences. They are fairly transparent. Once through them there is no more subtle barrier. She is honest and she doesn't flinch. I admire her for that. It's why I trust her.

We had rather a curious conversation. She asked me if I really wanted to take responsibility for the decision about whether or not to try more treatment. I was a little shocked. Did she still not understand? It's my life. I want to make the decisions. I need her to give me information and of course I value her opinion as the experienced expert, but the decision is mine. Cancer has taken so much away from my life, I don't want it to take everything. My brain still works. Let me retain something of my identity. Let me make decisions. She asked whether the responsibility was a burden. Of course not. I am quite prepared to live with my own decisions. It's not just the doctors who are trained to take responsibility! She pointed out that it would be easier if I let her make the decision

82

and then I could blame her if I got worse. It doesn't work like that. She knows it and so do I. She faltered even as she said it. I don't want to do it that way.

I know she is concerned for me, but she can't change the situation. She can't take this on for me. She can only be there with me and that's the hardest task of all. But she does it. I know she worries about my insistence on knowing so much. It's not the being told that hurts anyway, its the facts themselves and she can't magic them away. If only she could.

Her view was that I had had four different treatment regimes and none of them had worked. Now it was time to accept that. Her preferred option would be to stop further treatment. The time I had dreaded for so long had finally come. And I wasn't ready.

She knew I would find it difficult to accept what she said. She gave me time to talk about it. What about the other options? Well there was always the chance I might respond to chemotherapy. A continuous low dose alkalyting agent, not the kind that would make me sick or cause my hair to fall out, would do me little harm and just might reverse the disease. A very slight chance but it seemed the only hope to grasp at. I don't want to just give up. I can't. I feel well. I want to use that to fight while I still can. I know the situation is pretty desperate. I haven't responded to anything. Four different treatments and not one of them has worked. It doesn't matter that is probably because my tumour is growing slowly. It is still growing. It will get me in the end unless it is stopped.

My doctor suggested I have a CT scan. I knew she was expecting the tumours scattered round my abdomen to have grown. Why not? If it had grown in the scar the likelihood was that it was growing all over. But I felt so well. I couldn't trust that feeling any more though. I genuinely just didn't know. It should have grown, but maybe it hadn't. The uncertainty stretched unbearably on and on. Another week till the scan. Another week till the results.

The scan was the usual mix of farce and discomfort. Discomfort because of the swollen bladder and enema; the inept attempts to find a viable vein in my arm. Farce because they decided that my veins had disappeared because my hands were cold. They sent a junior nurse in search of a bowl to fill with warm water. The first bowl was too small. She was sent away again. She returned with the washing up bowl and filled it with near boiling water. Only afterwards did they think of warming all of me with a blanket.

Then another week to wait for the results. Long days, longer nights. Bit in the end the news was relatively good. The disease in the abdomen had hardly grown since January, certainly not anything like the same rate as under my arm. My doctor was calm and matter of fact, but a nurse told me she had cut short her holiday to be there to tell me the results. We spent most of the time talking about how we might organise the long planned support group. Maybe I had an indefinite future after all.

I found it difficult to accept the implications immediately, but yesterday my second opinion doctor confirmed the good news. The hormone treatment is perhaps responsible for the relative stability I have been enjoying. I should stay on it for the meantime, leaving chemotherapy for when or if the cancer starts growing in my abdomen again. He was his usual optimistic self. Refusing to despair, telling me of exciting new treatment possibilities. But I find it hard to believe in miracles these days. Despite the hopeful emphasis he is telling me the same thing. I have exhausted the established options.

Back to where we started. My horizons are a little more limited but not much. The future is indefinite again, but today I feel no joy. There is no instant recovery. I am just weary, doubtful. I'm sick of being resilient. Sick of being hit in the stomach and having to pick myself up all over again. Sick of trying to find the positive. Sick of it. Sick of it. What arrogance to feel anyone will be interested in reading about my petty agonies. Perhaps sleep will restore my equilibrium.

SUNDAY 29 OCTOBER 1989

These last two months really have taken their toll. Not just on me, on Paul too. I knew he had been under a lot of stress, but he talked about it as pressure of work so I didn't really understand. This morning we had one of those lazy mornings in bed, oblivious to all the tasks we ought to have done. We started to talk, just one of those catching up sessions we've been too busy for lately. Then more came out than we had foreseen. "Bark stripping" we call it. We still need to challenge each other, and so ourselves, but cancer has made us nicer. We don't have screaming rows about important things any more, just little things. Important things we talk about quietly but it still hurts.

Without our realising it something had almost died between us. We were still good friends, good companions, busy together and apart. But we were going through the motions, not really loving. It's happened so often before, but we're such good actors, and good friends, it takes a while to realise it. Suddenly everything seems drab and unexciting and we can't work out why. We try all sorts of descriptions, avoiding the right one until we find it accidentally.

Paul was so reluctant to tell me but I knew anyway. Fatigue has worn him down. This constant uncertainty, the ever present threat that I am going to die, has turned him away from me a little. It is so hard to remain committed to someone, not knowing whether they will be there in a few months or a few years time. I can understand that. And the uncertainty goes on and on and on. That tenderness when I was first

84

diagnosed couldn't possibly be sustained without a break for nearly four years. I didn't expect or want it to. It would have been easier if I had either died or been cured quickly but it just isn't like that.

In a sense Paul is going through the same painful process of adjusting to this latest progression that I have had. The same resentment to the sharp cutting off of a relaxed attitude to life and an indefinite future. Anger at the possibilities we can't choose any more. Being Paul he copes while everyone else has a crisis, then when they're recovering he goes down and no one understands.

He continues in all the outward signs of commitment, but that is not what I need. I know him too well. The more he is at his most active, making the most caring gestures, the less he his really there. He stops meeting my eyes.

It would be easier if I was less demanding, more oblivious, but I can't be. I have to be myself. More so perhaps now I am under threat. I don't have the time, the patience to be untrue. That is part of the problem too. It hasn't all been bad. Cancer has given me opportunities for self development and I have taken them with both hands. I know far more about who I am and what I want from life than I ever did before I was diagnosed. I go out and act on that knowledge far more than I ever did before. But Paul has suffered. For a long time he feels he has restrained in himself the very priorities I have given into. It was only last year that he started the Masters degree he had signed up for the year I was diagnosed. Some of it he has imposed on himself. I am very strong willed and I expect those around me to be equally so, to stand up for themselves if they want something. But Paul has been holding back, simply because I have cancer. I was angry when he said that, how could he be so patronising. I felt a little guilty too. I hadn't seen what was to my advantage not to see.

Some of it is a little jealousy. Here I am writing, getting published, which was always his dream. I can't hold myself back, and as he points out that would tear us apart even more effectively. He would feel guilty, I resentful. A classic no win situation. Change has happened and we cannot put the clock back.

There aren't any answers, not to be reasoned out anyway. Paul was right, I do try and solve everything rationally but sometimes that isn't appropriate. We have no plans for change. We've been here before. Paul has done what he can to establish his independence. It's the same old problem and there are no new solutions. But just talking is an answer of sorts, we both feel much closer than we have been for weeks. I wouldn't have said we were distant before. I only realise it now I see a new gentleness and lightheartedness in the way we react. Paul is walking round the house whistling, I giggle. We are both laughing more.

It is like the thoughts that were too terrible for Paul to share had become a barrier. I don't really want to talk in depth about his fears about how he will live without me. We joke about his predilection for long legged dumb blondes but that is as far as it goes. There are limits to what I want to share. I genuinely don't want him to mourn me for ever but I can't talk seriously about the new family I hope he will find. Touching the outlines without exploring the depths is enough. The talk we had this morning has freed not just him but me too. I'm not sure why. It's something to do with the fact that it acknowledges I am still me. That I may have cancer but I'm still the person Paul can talk to about anything, everything.

Curled up by the fire both of us are reluctant to break the spell. I think back all those years, to the Sundays in front of the open fire in our first cottage. Except it has changed. Then he wrote and I read. Now it is reserved.

15 NOVEMBER 1989

My writing has given me some understanding. Understanding has made me a little more tolerant of myself. I can give into pain because I know I will recover. I can accept that I am a cancer patient because I know that will not threaten the areas of my life where cancer is irrelevant. I don't have to climb so many mountains and I can join a support group. I know myself better. I know I need to sometimes work with the fact I have cancer, to face it, explore it, probe it. But sometimes I need to do the complete opposite. I need to ignore it, to confirm that I can be valued, loved, for what I am and what I can do, not just because I have cancer.

I realise how important these quite contradictory strategies have been. I have been rather reluctant to acknowledge them both. To concentrate on areas of my life where cancer was irrelevant seemed to be taking the easy option, backing away from a problem I ought to face. I have found that if I didn't get away I would never have found the strength to face it directly. Denial, escapism, distraction, call it what you will. They are rather grudging, disparaging words for something which is really quite life giving and constructive. It's less a matter of fighting cancer, more about building myself up. Same objective, just a difference in emphasis.

I look back on these recent diary entries and wonder whether they are worth including in a book. They are repetitive, tedious even. I don't like my style. It seems so self satisfied. It's hard to write about myself without self justification creeping in. All that pain matters only to me, not to anyone else. All that agonizing. I just don't feel like that any more. Yet it is closer to the experience than anything I could write now about what happened. Maybe I should share it. Someone else might read it when they were down, just like I searched for a writer who understood. Then they could see yes it hurts but it does get better. You start to look beyond the pain, get absorbed, caught up in real life and then wonder why it all felt so terrible.

I am developing a love hate relationship with this book. I think of incidents, phrases, changes, at odd moments. Walking home from work, in the car, doing the garden. I want that space for other thoughts. They have to be connected with my cancer but not so much with me. I am in danger of boring myself. I want to mull over other ways of writing and drawing on my experience. How shall we develop the support group? Who will be involved? How? What will I say at the conference in front of all those doctors? What are the practical ways cancer services could be improved? I seem to be developing contacts with people who will listen to what I have to say, who are in a position to change things and I need to sort out my ideas.

Writing this has been the means of being able to understand a process. I needed more than a diary, immediate recall to rid myself of hurt and confusion. I wasn't patient enough to simply record everything as it happened. Perceptions were my interest not events anyway. Writing started out as a solitary, rather scurrilous activity. Something done secretly, privately, to rid myself of a seething backlog of emotion. Then it became material for analysis, a tool for understanding. It grew into an exercise in creativity. I found I enjoyed searching for the right words to describe how I felt. Now I worry that vanity is taking over. Perhaps it is time to stop.

My diary has changed over the years. I have learned to express myself better, to write less selfconsciously when it really hurts. I can write as it happens now, not just afterwards. I think that is progress. It took so much time. The first versions of the early chapters which were written so quickly left out a lot of the pain. It was only added in the course of many repeated rewrites, a sentence here, a sentence there; a few painful experiences I had "forgotten". Gradually the picture became a little more shadowed and I became more satisfied that it represented honestly what I had felt.

Because I am closer to the experience I am becoming less interested in drawing it together as a coherent account. I am also beginning to see patterns repeat. I am concerned at the effort needed to impose a structure. I can't just write about everything yet perhaps I am distorting the experience by writing about it however honest I try to be. Reporting, by definition, has to be selective; yet selection diminishes the original. Already I seem to remember less about the early days and more about what I have written about them. It is like taking photographs. You remember what you see in the picture not what happened.

Perhaps working on this book encourages me to dwell on a side of my life which is ultimately not that important. I realise it cuts out so much of my experience over the last three and a half years, things that have essentially nothing to do with cancer though of course they were

87

touched by it. My relationship with Paul, with the friends who not only lived through all this but who encouraged me to write about it. The things we did, that we talked about, that don't feature here. I just don't know how to capture them. It is easier to find words to describe pain than normal life. People, places, events. I don't know how to write about them but I want to be able to acknowledge their place at the centre of things.

If I had to list my most vivid memories of the last three months they would include very little of what is here. I see rather walks with friends across the Downs; standing on Devil's Dyke in a howling gale; getting out of bed to play Cluedo till the early hours of the morning like furtive children. I see Paul's wicked delight in accidentally setting fire to a box of fireworks at a party in Norfolk. I see myself jumping over a fence on a winter afternoon to run towards the sun. Having cancer is in the end quite incidental to my life. It's nothing more than a mechanism. Some gains, some losses, but I still don't want it to take over. Being cured of cancer, or dying of it, aren't the most crucial alternatives. Whatever happens I will die eventually. The real choice is between living or merely surviving.

I don't need to write about having cancer as a means of understanding myself any more. This book is finished but I have an article to write on "What I want from my cancer doctor" for an international medical conference next year. Perhaps other teaching sessions on breaking bad news for medical students. There is the support group to be set up. It will need a great deal of work. Of course I will be busy but stretched not stressed. I have learnt the importance of balance, that I need to be busy and outgoing but that I need to allow myself time and peace and leisure too.

At least that is the theory. Of course it just doesn't work like that. My life is not as ordered and rational as I sometimes like to believe. I frequently get too involved in too many things, all very enjoyable in themselves but together too hectic. It is less that I make time for what is important, more that every so often I am forced to see I have left it out. I rarely take time to write, it's more something I turn to when I am ill or exhausted and take to my bed. Why then? I sometimes feel I am too hard on myself, too easily seduced by all the petty tasks I ought to do and enjoy doing. I dismiss the need to take time to be self indulgent, to dream, to write, to meditate. Or is it that I am too easy on myself? It is also hard work. It needs intense concentration, sometimes it involves confronting issues it is easier to ignore. I find myself resisting, finding excuses, even though I know I will feel stronger when I have made the effort.

Writing has finally taught me the limitations of analysis. Sometimes the outlines are not clearly defined. I am not going to reach a single point of resolution. I have been suffering under the delusion that one day I would understand, that if I worked away at it hard enough I would

88

reach enlightenment like some oriental mystic. I am discovering that insight is a process not an event.

Contradictions have to be lived with. It's just another kind of uncertainty. It is not a question of anger or acceptance, defiance or defeat, confrontation or denial, hope or despair. They are all there, sometimes in sequence, sometimes together. I am learning to live with ambivalence. I am never going to be able to neatly categorise my reaction to this disease. There is not going to be a final coming to terms with cancer, with death. Equilibrium can be approached but never arrived at. Not for me. Then I really would be dead.

I look back and wonder why I'm still here, Maybe I'm just lucky, maybe I've been fortunate enough to have the kind of cancer that grows slowly. That feels such an inadequate explanation. I want to say it wasn't just luck it was hard work. It certainly fits the model expounded by all those books I read on "alternative" methods. I refused to let cancer get the better of me, I fought and I accepted it, and although I wasn't cured I stayed well. I am also wary of that as an exclusive explanation. What about all those people I have known who had the same attitude and who died? I can't reject the biological aspects entirely. I guess I just have to live with the fact there are no clear alternatives here either.

I really wanted to write one of those happy ever after books after all. I had planned to end with the last chapter, taking off for New Zealand, long before I wrote it. Not exactly cured but having outlived my prognosis by some years and with an indefinite future ahead. It had a clarity that seemed appropriate for a book. Beginning with diagnosis, ending exactly three years later with a new beginning. But for most of us living with cancer just isn't like that. It's about living with uncertainty. Not knowing from week to week, from month to month what the future holds; whether the disease will get better or worse, develop quickly or slowly, respond or not respond to treatment.

I just don't know whether I will be here next year or the year after or the year after that. I know it's true for everyone but for most people would consider it only occasionally. It's very different living with that knowledge as an ever present reality. I can see the advantages in being more spontaneous, but I'd rather that it wasn't forced on me because I simply cannot plan ahead.

Confronting one's own mortality is never easy, it can't be. Death negates all we value, all we are. Except growth and change. To have them we need beginnings and endings, however painful. That's all death will be, an ending. Until the last there will still be perfect days as well as some painful ones. I know now that pain hurts but it doesn't last. If the disease gets worse I'm not going to enter a whole new way of being called dying. My life will just continue until it stops.

Why me? I have found my answer. Because death happens to us all. I am not yet special, privileged, exempt. No one is, not even me. But not yet God, not yet.

EPILOGUE

Friends all say "but you can't stop there". Maybe they're right, it does leave out some of the best parts of the story. We did set up the support group, it's been up and running for more than a year now. I think its made a difference for patients, I know its made a difference for the staff. I've seen it in their manner, their way of talking to patients. They understand more, they demonstrate that understanding more. For me too there have been changes. In the course of developing the group the staff who treat me have become my friends. I even plucked up the courage to call my doctor by her first name. It seemed such a momentous decision at the time. It was ridiculous though, I felt, to be on first name terms with everyone else except her. I remember well the initial nervous nonchalance, but now it seems right and natural. We have become as near friends as doctor and patient can be. She needs a little distance, is wary of getting too close to be able to operate efficiently, and I respect that. But it gives a stability, a centre to my life as a patient that was not there before.

And yes, I did speak at that international medical conference and was well received. And there have been other conferences, other publications. They represent such little victories really. There are other parts of the story untold too. I have been ill, on a couple of occasions very ill and near to death. On the other hand there have been many months with cancer very much in the background.

So why am I not writing still? Its very simple. I have no need to. I have sometimes resorted to paper to sort through my pain or rage at a difficult time but there is no urge to continue the book. The events are new but the experience is essentially the same. I have nothing more to say. I found my answer: that there is no answer. Pain is part of the world, and why it is unevenly distributed is beyond my understanding. To create meaning out of suffering is within my grasp though. It is still my choice.

That implies I see the question of survival at the centre of my life. But its not true. That's not what I want to say. The fact that the cancer is more advanced is not why I've stopped writing. Whether or not cancer is the mechanism, my life will have a beginning, a middle, and an end. My life is what is important, not the manner or timing of my death.

Maybe I'm just lazy. Its a long time since I've written about having cancer. The more it makes me ill the more it becomes essential to focus on living. That means just accepting the days as they go, good or bad. No recording the experience, no assessing it, just being.

It is easier to write about conflict, and there is little conflict now, either between me and my doctor, or between me and fate, or about whether or not I die of cancer. That sounds boring; what it really means is that I am happy. And to misquote Tolstoy, happiness is a pretty uninteresting story.

That the end is acceptance, not being free of cancer, was something I resisted for so long. Its a funny kind of acceptance though. Acceptance of life and all it entails, but not of death. The idea that one day I will simply cease to exist and the world will continue without me still seems sometimes like an obscene black joke. I am no longer angry about dying but the little daily losses and frustrations, the things I can no longer do, are sometimes hard to bear. There is no desire to make a pattern of it though; I know that some days I will be angry, some sad, and some quite calm about it, relieved there is no need to struggle further. The important thing is just to ride out the bad days, to create as much potential as possible for the happy times.

In the end there is a certain circularity about it all. Here I am, five years after the diagnosis, lying in my garden on a warm spring day. Birdsong, trees, sun, peace. That's all that matters.

APRIL 1991

Afterword

Paul Dennison

Anne died on the 17th of July, 1992 at about 12.30 in the afternoon. She died the way she had wanted to: in my arms, in her own bed at home and without great pain. She had been house-bound for about ten days, and had been on oxygen and morphine for about five weeks. Her final relapse was sudden, and mercifully short.

Six weeks before she died, she and I had a short break with friends in a sixteenth century manor-house in Cornwall. It was the last week in May and the weather was fine. The countryside seemed not only green but new. Anne was sufficiently active to go for gentle walks of an hour or more, and to swim in the family pool.

By the time we returned to London, she was again suffering breath-lessness, and a build-up of fluid in the pleural cavity, the recurrence of something which had happened several times in the last year. Generally this had resulted in a hospital stay where litres of body fluid, sometimes as much as ten or fifteen, were drawn off before the build-up was neutralised.

During this hospital admission, I made an appointment to see Anne's doctor. I asked her the question which Anne and I had stopped asking after the early days, partly because it seemed crass, and also because with cancer it is a question impossible to answer. How long did she think that Anne had to live?

'Not long. Probably only weeks.'

'I need to know if you can tell me. I can have extended leave from work to look after Anne -- they're very supportive -- but I could probably only do that once. Is this the end?'

'Yes. I think it is.'

I surprised myself by briefly bursting into tears. I was braced for this news, of course, but even so, my reaction was immediate. I was grateful to the doctor for being so candid, because it meant I was clear on what I should do.

Anne and I had discussed dying quite a lot. I remember saying to her "Right now, it's like you're skiing down a run -- you can't ski back -- but we can still make sure you take the best line. It's important to die the right way -- we can do that much."

93

Anne's doctor helped organise matters, so that as soon as it was feasible, Anne returned home. The local GP practice supplied Anne with a nurse-aide who visited once a day. St Christopher's Hospice sent two health visitors who were able to advise on matters on a weekly basis. They loaned equipment -- a commode for her bedroom and a wheel-chair for getting about a few precious days longer.

Anne's brother John flew over from Adelaide to be with her as did her sister Julie from Dunedin, our old home town. My parents visited, so for a time, the house was quite crowded.

Those last days were full of contrasts. Anne's physical condition deteriorated. Her breathlessness increased and she had to choose her words with care. Drugs and oxygen cylinders were required with greater frequency and her sleep was often difficult through being unable to lie down comfortably.

***

Looking back on that final year, we seem to have led an almost frenetic existence: snatches of intense happiness between periods of darkness and occasional irony.

--Anne, sitting on the beach north of Paphos, on Cyprus, watching the sun set over the sea and feeling wistful. Me, wandering restlessly up and down, snapping photographs.

--Anne collapsed on the first day of a short holiday in Venice, and was taken by water-ambulance from St Mark's Square through the Arsenal to a hospital on the north side. A grave, white-haired doctor ushered me out into the corridor and asked politely if I knew my wife had cancer? Did she know? At the time I found this comical.

--Going to Covent Garden to see 'Manon' with Viviana Durante and Irek Mukhamedov dancing the leading roles. Drinking champagne in the Crush Bar at half time.

--Attending the Christmas Party of the Cancer Patients' Support Group which Anne had helped set up at her hospital, which was now meeting regularly once a month.

--Picking up the phone one morning before leaving to visit Anne in hospital, to be asked by an unknown woman in the Department of Health if Anne had received a letter from Downing Street recently? "They want to give her an OBE, and we need to confirm that she'll accept. It's for the New Year's Honours list." I told her that Anne was in hospital but that she had a phone next to her bed. I gave her the number. Later Anne told me she was sure it was a hoax by one of her work colleagues, and for a long time she refused to take the call seriously.

--Having our Renault 5 checked by security police for bombs, before driving it into the courtyard of Buckingham Palace, and parking among the limousines. After the ceremony, at which Anne received the OBE from the Queen, we went to the Ritz to have a celebration luncheon with friends ...

***

A couple of days before she died, Anne told me about a day-dream she had in the afternoon. She imagined herself in a bare valley, a desolation. There were no trees, no birds, no breeze. Everything was still. In the distance she could see the shining of a river. She felt herself very much alone, steadily descending to the valley floor. I said it must be the valley of death. I think she agreed. She wouldn't tell me more.

One of the last things Anne said, the day before her death, was "Don't forget me."

Paul Dennison, 1995

APPENDICES

From THE GUARDIAN

Wednesday, March 29, 1989

WEDNESDAY WOMEN 17 **FIRST PERSON**

Coping with a terminal illness like cancer isn't just about pain and misery

SWEET LIFE IN THE SHADOW

Anne Dennison

SOON after I was diagnosed as having cancer I read several autobiographical accounts by those who had survived the experience which concluded: "I'm glad I had cancer." I thought they were insane. Either that or they were lucky enough to have a good prognosis and didn't need to take death seriously. I realise I have changed. I still can't go that far. But I begin to understand what they mean. There are positive aspects.

My cancer has refused to respond to treatment. We're running out of options and I know the disease will probably kill me. I once described it as feeling like one of those cartoon characters who comes to the edge of a cliff and keeps on going very well until he looks down and falls. I regret that image. It is so negative, so fearful.

Sometimes it feels more like I am carrying round a terrible and beautiful secret. The knowledge I will die makes me feel more alive than ever.

Even in the beginning I had to cope with a great deal all at once: advanced cancer, major surgery and chemotherapy. My world collapsed: the vision of myself as a 31 year old immortal disappeared. I was numb with shock. Bewildered more than angry. "What had I done to deserve this?"

To survive I shut out the world for a while. I became very aware of small delights like the sensuous joy of lying in my garden in the summer sun to convalesce. I sometimes thought I must be mad. Everyday things gave me so much happiness. I felt more conscious of beauty, colour, warmth than ever before. Mind you, there were days when even finishing a novel seemed a hopeless waste of time.

My feeling for people too was heightened. I realised how important certain individuals were to me. Many learned to express their feelings for me as never before. That was awkward at first, now it has become part of our lives.

98

But there was a down side to that exhilaration. A conscious wanting to hold a precious minute. I couldn't always forget myself. Sometimes when most intensely enjoying this or that moment with this or that person. I wanted to stop time. I was very aware such happiness might never come again.

I felt panic. It seemed I was only beginning to make my way in the world and sort out my role in life. There was so much unfinished, so much I needed to sort out. I was given time for a few major projects and completions. But I worried about the point of it all. Nothing I did was really going to make much difference. What was the point of starting something I might not live long enough to finish.

Two and a half years on the panic has passed. My body has cried wolf too often. Despite the ups and downs of my illness and the cancer not responding to treatment, I am still here. I often think how reassured I would have been in those early days if I could have seen myself now. I have lived to see so many of the things I never thought possible. I still have some problems in talking comfortably about the future but I have largely lost the qualms I had about making appointments a few months hence.

I have learned to assume I shall be there. Completing major projects is no longer important, but beginning them is. Now I find I have come full circle. I am again very aware of the present. But there is a difference. I seem to have retained an intense enjoyment of life but lost the painful self-consciousness I had before.

Having had sufficient time to regain my assumption of the future has helped. Even if my doctors haven't cured me they have given me that, and I am grateful. Time has also given me the opportunity to assess what is really important. My life is much more focussed. Every day has to matter and I go to great pains to ensure it does.

I have discovered some of my friends slightly envy the depth of my new found enjoyment of life. They would like to concentrate on what they feel is important but lack my excuse. They would like to take risks but feel they have more to lose. What others see as courageous on my part would probably be seen as foolhardy on theirs.

On the other hand I envy them too. I can sometimes waste time and be lighthearted. But I do feel I lack a certain innocence, an ability to be totally careless about today because there is always tomorrow! I am left with a continuing sense of urgency, a need to make today count. That can mean finding unexpected pleasures in the minutiae of daily life and impatience with them at the same time. Sometimes I wish I could get my delusion of immortality back again.

Those who are closest to me do try to understand how I feel and talk to me about it occasionally. But others tell me they know exactly how I feel. They don't ask me how I am any more: they tell me I look well.

Sometimes they avoid me altogether. I become inhibited too. I don't know how to tell them that living with a possibly terminal illness isn't just about pain and misery. Yet perhaps they are the ones who need to know it most.

****

PERSONAL VIEW

'Knowledge, belief, and hope'

Anne Dennison

British Medical Journal, Volume 298, 10 June 1989

I know that it is highly unlikely that I shall live more than a few years. I have late stage cancer which has not responded well to treatment. I have insisted from the beginning on knowing as much as possible about what is happening to me. That includes my prognosis as well as the precise details of the available treatment choices.

Wouldn't I rather not know? Definitely not. I am still angry with those doctors who took it on themselves to protect and patronise me with evasive replies to difficult questions. I have learnt something that my doctors find difficult to understand. The anxiety of uncertainty and the constant churning through a multitude of possibilities are much harder to bear than dealing with bad news and a much more limited range of probabilities. I have found that hope is much easier to maintain when it does not have to cover the whole spectrum from complete cure to imminent death.

The alternative to knowledge is not blissful ignorance. If I did not know my prognosis where would I be? In that awful state I was in before I asked probably. I was deeply suspicious that more was going on than I was being told. Why wasn't I being told, was it so bad? Not nearly as bad as my worst fears as it turned out. I used to lie awake at night mulling the possibilities over and over. I scared myself by reading outdated medical texts. I was frightened to broach a subject that my doctors were so obviously avoiding. That agonising took so much out of me. I don't have time for such anxieties any more; I'm much too busy making the most of each and every day. I wasted so much time and energy wondering; merely coping with bad news is so much easier. I'd have had to know I was dying one day. I am glad I was given the opportunity to face the pain that knowledge initially brings with sufficient time and health to make something meaningful of it.

* * *

I don't confront the facts directly all the time. Denial is mercifully strong still. I cope by refusing to believe them. The distinction between knowledge and belief keeps me sane.

Sometimes knowledge and belief run in sequence. More perhaps in the early days; one minute despairing at my chances of survival, the next full of angry confidence that I would prove them wrong. Now, although my chances are worse, I am more relaxed in my fight. These days it is more as if I am operating on two levels at once. Part of me knows that my cancer is likely to kill me, part of me believes that it won't happen.

...Living each day as if it were your last is intoxicating but trying in my experience.

Living with contradiction has not been an easy lesson to learn. But it is terribly important. It enables me to get the most out of today by assuming a future. I can prioritise choices as if the worse predictions were true even though I refuse to believe them. But I avoid living as if tomorrow was literally the only future I could count on. Living each day as if it were your last is intoxicating but trying in my experience.

Of course, knowing my prognosis gave me great pain. But there was much more than despair. I became aware how much life meant to me. Now I make time for the people and things that are important. That awareness and those changes add a great deal to my life. Coming to terms with what I know has for me been a circular process. Confronting the worst possibility has enabled me to face it without fear. I feel sorry for those patients who don't know. They live with debilitating uncertainty, too, but where can they find the strength to cope with it?

My belief is not to be dismissed as a comforting delusion, it is after all tempered by knowledge. Of course, it can easily be destroyed by a reminder of how heavily the cards are stacked against me, that I am a patient whether I like it or not. I shall be desperately disappointed if my belief is eventually unfounded, but I feel I shall be able to cope with that disappointment because I knew that might be the outcome a long time ago. I have had time to come to terms with it. I shall give up my belief only when I really am near death. Right now I need it to live a full and active life.

* * *

So I tell my doctors, my family, and friends don't deny me knowledge. To protect me from a painful truth denies me the chance of finding the resources needed to resist and cope with it. And don't deny me my belief even if you can't reconcile it with your knowledge. I want more than the scant comfort of a vague hope which is all the most rational among you will allow. I can gain a sudden occasional lift from hearing of someone who beat the odds or a promising development of new technology but that is hardly enough to sustain me.

You, too, have your defences. When the going gets rough don't retreat into belief and pretend that the facts don't exist. Answer my questions honestly. Let me talk about dying occasionally, though I know it's hard for you. I'd be the same if the positions were reversed. You don't have to face it now so why should you. I can take a little denial from all of you some of the time and from some of you all of the time. But once in a while I need to share my knowledge with those who are close to me.

Please recognise the changes that my knowledge has brought. Stop trying to encourage me to be exactly as I was before the diagnosis. Just because I am physically well doesn't mean I want to live as I did then. Try and understand why it's important to me to work at a less stressful job and make more time for my family and friends. I know it's hard for you to live with the constant reminders that something is never going to be the same again. But it's hard for me too. I was perfectly happy with my lifestyle before I had cancer. While appreciating the gains that my new priorities have given me I, too, regret the lost chances and career opportunities. So stop reminding me of them. I can't do as you encourage me and just carry on as if nothing had happened.

The price of knowledge is high, it cannot be unlearnt, only forgotten. I am happy for us all to forget sometimes, we all need the respite. But don't deny it because that separates us and cuts me off from what gives me my greatest strength.

Anne Dennison is a civil servant from London.

****

WHAT DO I WANT FROM MY CANCER DOCTOR? A PATIENT'S VIEW

by Anne Dennison

I think it is most appropriate that I was asked to speak on the subject of what I want from my doctor at a conference on Cancer and the Mind. Because what I want from my doctor more than anything else is the recognition that I have a mind. The mind is the basis of identity, of individuality. It distinguishes the person from the patient.

A diagnosis of cancer, any potentially fatal illness, is a serious threat to one's sense of self. The last thing I need is to be treated in such a way that my identity is challenged still further. I need a person oriented rather than a patient oriented system of medical care. I would like to talk about four main aspects which I think are relevant to a more person centred approach.

Firstly information

The need to share information, information about the disease, the treatment and the prognosis.

Secondly, sensitive systems of patient management. The need for systems and structures which recognise just how vulnerable cancer patients are.

Thirdly, emotional care. The need to provide emotional care alongside medical care, preferably as an integral part of it.

Fourthly, self help. The importance of doctors encouraging their patients to do what they can to help themselves as part of the treatment process.

But let me begin by talking briefly about how it felt to become a cancer patient. I had never been seriously ill before. I didn't know how to be a patient. More importantly, for about the first time in my life I just didn't know how to deal with the situation. I was so stunned by the diagnosis I didn't have the initiative or the assertiveness I needed to overcome the helplessness I felt. I was angry with myself at the time, I don't understand myself now.

Perhaps I can make myself clearer by referring to the areas where I've said patients need a more person-centred approach.

Take information, for instance. When I was diagnosed I expected doctors to give me all the information I needed. When I was found to have an ovarian cyst, a very nice young doctor told me I should have it out because "it will continue to grow and cause you trouble." It was a busy outpatients' clinic. I knew there were patients already undressed

103

in the cubicles either side of me and he seemed to be implying it was all very routine. I assumed that meant it was benign. I asked about when it was likely to be done and we talked about how the waiting list worked. Then he looked at his watch and said "Any more questions?" I said "I don't think so" and the consultation was over. I got dressed and only then started to think. I hadn't thought in advance about what questions I should ask. But now I began to wonder. He was talking about an operation in a month or so. Did that mean it was urgent? Did that mean there was a chance it was malignant? Surely not. He would have said so. By now I had left the clinic. Should I go back and ask to see him again? Oh, but I couldn't. Should I ring and ask to speak to the doctor I had seen before? But they were so busy. I didn't want to be a nuisance. I couldn't make a fuss. Well I continued agonizing for a month. Then at last I was called up for the operation and I asked whether it was possible the cyst was malignant. "Yes" I was told. I had asked a direct question and got a direct answer. Unfortunately no one had told me those were the rules and it took me a long while to work them out.

Accepting that I might have cancer and then that I did have cancer was not an easy process. but it was a lot easier than living with agonizing uncertainty and the constant mulling through of a whole multitude of possibilities. It was so debilitating. I wasted so much time.

Even after I was diagnosed there were lots of questions I didn't ask my doctor but where I would have found it helpful to know the answer. They were of two kinds. There were the questions I didn't ask because I didn't have enough basic information. I never asked, for example, about whether or not there were any alternative treatments to what I was initially offered because it never occurred to me that different doctors could treat exactly the same type of disease in very different ways. It seems incredible to me now but it was how I felt then. I suppose it was just my lack of experience as a patient.

The other kind of questions I didn't know how to ask were those where I was very scared of the answer. It took me many months to insist on answers to questions about my prognosis and what might be done if the treatment I was having didn't work. I wanted to know before then but I got it into my head that because my doctors avoided the subject, or gave me evasive answers, the news must be absolutely terrible. I was too scared to ask but I had to know. In the end I tried to work out the answers myself by reading outdated textbooks. It was a painful experience without the interpretation and reassurance my doctor later provided.

How can you make it easier? I would like to see doctors move away from the idea that information should only be given to patients in the form of answers to questions. Waiting for patients to ask presupposes a quite unreal degree of knowledge and initiative. I would rather see information freely offered. I know myself what a difference it made when I met a doctor who began by saying "Let me explain what I think is happening to you." If a doctor is unsure about whether or not his patient wants to know something the onus should be on the doctor to do the asking, not the patient. Doctors ought to ask the questions, such as, for example, "Would you like me to talk about the other options for treatment?" or "Are you worried it might be cancer?"

The way information is given needs careful thought. A shocked or upset patient may not be in a fit state to remember details as I know only too well. Written information can be useful not only for reinforcing what has already been said but for giving patients an information base from which to develop their own questions.

One interesting experiment I read about recently involved the tape recording of the consultation where the patient was told of the cancer diagnosis and the proposed treatment. The patient was then given the recording to take away, to listen to again at leisure. Some also played it to relatives and friends. The evaluation concluded that both patients and their families benefitted enormously. Twenty per cent did find listening to the tapes upsetting, though everyone said they found them helpful. (1) Patients know better than their doctors that while bad news may be upsetting, it is still better to know and discuss it fully.

Another innovation involved the doctor writing a summary of a consultation on a piece of paper to which a carbon was attached. One copy went on the patient's file as a record of the discussion, the other was given to the patient. It seems so simple. Why isn't it standard practice?

Using published information is also useful. I've recently seen patients with that dazed look of the newly diagnosed coming out of

consultation rooms at my own hospital with BACUP booklets firmly clutched in their hands. I envy them. When I was diagnosed there was no readily available information. When I asked one doctor how I could find out more about ovarian cancer he told me "Well, you're capable of reading the textbooks". Fine. but they weren't exactly accessible on the shelves of the libraries and bookshops of suburban south London. I didn't like to ask if I could borrow his. I was just lucky. A friend of a friend was a medical student.

Different patients have different information needs. I want to know everything that is relevant because I want to take final responsibility for treatment decisions. "It's my life and I want to stay in charge of it!!" Cancer takes away so much, to not encourage me to retain responsibility adds insult to injury. Of course I listen to what my doctors have to say and I rely very much on their advice but I feel it should be up to me to make the most important decisions. Of course they are difficult decisions to make, but having someone else take the responsibility isn't going to make them easier to live with. Quite the contrary.

I do need to rely totally on my doctor for information though. I cannot make good decisions unless I know all the relevant facts. I need to know about side effects of drugs because that affects my decision as to whether or not I should take them. I need to know what their success rates are because that affects whether or not I judge them to be worth the side effects. Weighing risks against benefits is a very individual equation and I have no wish to let someone else do it on my behalf. Even my doctor.

I am told other patients are different, and that many do not wish to take on as much responsibility. I am unsure whether or not that means they really are content to hand over to someone else. Perhaps it means that they have never been invited to take responsibility and are too frightened to demand it from their doctors.

Giving fuller information will not be easy. Ducking the issue, by being if not outright dishonest then "economical with the truth", may help the doctor but it doesn't help the patient. The patient will find out sooner or later and then feels betrayed. "Why didn't they tell me. Why? I trusted him" they say. I'm very glad I've never again met the doctor who told me I ought to have that cyst removed "Because it will continue to grow and cause you trouble". I still don't trust him. And I cannot be the patient of a doctor I do not trust.

Honesty is perhaps the most important quality I look for in a doctor. Sometimes that means admitting you don't know the answer. Trust your patients. I admire and respect a doctor who tells me he doesn't know the answer to my question. It's much better than trying to bluff through the issue. Perhaps I can give you an example. When I was told I had cancer one of my first questions was "How long have I got?". I had seen all the movies; this was the cue for the doctor to say "six months". But none of the doctors I met in the early days would talk in terms of time; they would just pat me on the arm and waffle on about chemotherapy having an excellent chance of curing me. I was convinced time was so short that they were all hiding the information from me. I realise now what they were hiding was not some awful and unspeakable truth but simply the fact that it is just not possible to exactly estimate an individual's chances of survival. They just didn't know the answer to my question. If only someone had explained and talked me through the averages.

Volunteering information without waiting for specific questions is one way of tackling a very real communication gap between doctors and patients. Another way of addressing the problem is to look at ways of encouraging patients to express their own individual needs more clearly. I have to say my own experience of inpatient and outpatient routines has lead me to the conclusion that many of them are a positive hindrance to good communication.

Perhaps I can illustrate from my own experience of outpatient departments. I spent many anxious hours in them, trying not to worry "what they might find this time", and mentally listing my questions over and over. My inevitable nervousness was made worse by a constant tension, never knowing whether or not I would be called next or in an hour's time. Many times when I actually saw a doctor my desire for information was in conflict with my having had enough and my need to escape to real life, to home or to work. I remember the difference when the delay was not only explained but an apology given as well. It was a small courtesy but it had a profound effect. I had even been given a rough idea of how long I would have to wait so I wandered off for a cup of coffee and settled down with my book. Of course I was still nervous but I was relaxed enough to have a coherent conversation with my doctor. I had been treated as a human being and I found I could talk easily and frankly about the questions which worried me.

Getting past the waiting room is only the first hurdle. The next step is being called to see the doctor. Under one system I was called into an examination room by a nurse. There I was asked to "strip from the waist down". Often I was left alone for a good half four to wait for the doctor, sitting on the couch in a small cell lit by a high window. If I forgot to bring something to read I listened to the conversation the doctor was having with the patient next door and I worried. I was very aware of how busy the doctor was, with another patient waiting on the other side too. Little wonder I had trouble getting my questions out when he did appear. contrast the system I met at another hospital, where the doctor only had one consultation and examination suite occupied at a time. He stepped out of it to call each new patient himself.

There were other factors in this second system which made communication easier too. I actually got to talk to the doctor with my clothes on. Anyone who says that isn't important has never been a gynaecology patient. I don't know if any of you have ever tried to either listen to what your doctor is saying or to ask questions when you're lying flat on your back with your legs in the air but take it from me it isn't easy. Even in a gown sitting on an examination couch it is difficult to get my questions out. In my clothes I am more myself and less the tongue-tied patient.

Patients need a clear separation between consultation and examination if they are to communicate effectively. Ideally consultation and examination should be conducted in separate rooms. I know I can talk more easily when they are. If they have to take place in the same room then let them be two quite separate parts of the meeting. Yes it will take a little more time though my doctor usually uses it to write up my notes. Is the few seconds that it takes a patient to slip off the necessary clothing too much to ask? My GP sees many more patients per session than my hospital consultant, but there would be an outcry if he required all his patients to strip and be lined up in examination rooms before he spoke to them.

107

Another factor which I feel enhances communication is allowing the patient to bring a relative or friend to the consultation. I have found that when I'm upset I don't always remember my carefully rehearsed questions, or the answers. Staff at some hospitals seem to routinely ask patients whether or not they would like to bring in their husband, wife or whoever is sitting with them; others don't. I notice the question is more often asked where the processes of consultation and examination are separated. It is easier to take a relative or friend into a consultation than an examination. Of course not every patient will wish to share their consultation in this way, but it is a lot easier to decline the invitation than to pluck up courage to just take someone in with you to an examination room.

To those doctors who say it's all very well but I don't have the time to run my outpatients system like that, all I can say is: please make the time; your patients need it badly. And systems which make it difficult for patients to ask questions do not in the end save time anyway. Unasked questions simply get stored up as resentment. Complaints and angry outbursts take a lot longer to sort out.

I cannot emphasise too much just how bewildering and disconcerting the process of becoming a patient is. Patients need their doctors to explain how the system operates, to reassure them that they can ring the hospital if they are worried. What is more they need to know who they can ring, and when, and where. I think you will find few patients abuse such permission. You will find that even with this reassurance they will agonize about ringing up between appointments when things go wrong or if they should bother the doctor with their "trivial" questions.

Again I am returning to the theme that being a cancer patient leaves a person stunned, shocked and lacking initiative. Their medical care needs to take this into account. They need information, they need appropriate systems for delivering that information and they need their doctors to understand what they are going through.

What is more, doctors don't need to just understand, they need to communicate that they understand. Becoming a cancer patient is frightening and lonely. When I was diagnosed I felt that none of the staff who were treating me wanted to know how I felt. For four days I lay in bed and all any of the staff would talk about was my physical symptoms. One nurse did come and sit on my bed the day after I learned of the diagnosis and said "You must be feeling awful. Thinking why me? Why me?" I nodded. She patted my arm and said she'd come back later to talk about it but I never saw her again. One doctor bounced in and said "How are you feeling today?" His mistake. I said "I just feel absolutely devastated. I don't think it's really sunk in yet." He nodded and looked away. He prodded my stomach, muttered something to the nurse about the catheter and the drip and then left. I was extremely hurt. This was a doctor who had treated me for some months and I thought we had got on well. I felt I was now being punished, that somehow I had let him down by turning out to have cancer. I know he felt helpless and distressed but his way of showing it didn't help me.

Doctors do not always have the time, the energy or the inclination to provide emotional support to their patients. But again I emphasise they have more initiative than people who are sick and frightened. If doctors can't do it themselves it is their responsibility to set up a system of care which gives patients the opportunity to express how they feel, a system which recognises that the provision of emotional care is just as important a part of treatment as injecting drugs. Recognition of emotional needs and the provision of support is I think more important than ever in the current climate of increasing honesty and openness about cancer. More and more doctors are talking to their patients about their disease, the side effects of treatment, and their prognosis. This is right, but honesty without emotional support leaves patients to bear a heavy burden of knowledge alone.

What can be done to ensure emotional support is provided? Perhaps a nurse could be trained in counselling skills. That nurse also needs to be given specific and sufficient time to provide emotional support to patients. Another way of providing support is by enabling patients to support each other, perhaps by setting up a support group. I was shocked to find when I did a little research just how few hospital based groups there are. The need for them has never been greater. Fewer and fewer patients spend long weeks as in-patients these days. As outpatients they may miss the emotional support it is possible to provide in a well-run ward.

Support groups and specialist counselling are undoubtedly helpful but there is no real substitute for a patient knowing that her own doctor is willing to understand what it feels like. I am rather at a loss to explain why it is so important, I just know it is. I know that the acknowledgement my doctor gives me that she understands how I feel is what I value most. I suppose having cancer is the most traumatic thing that has ever happened to me. Sharing that experience creates intimacy, with my family, with my friends, and with my doctor.

Sometimes the relationship is two way. Occasionally it is nice to know how my doctor feels too. I remember still the young houseman who sat on my bed at 2 am one morning. We talked about how I felt. Then he talked about how he felt. He told me what a difficult patient he found me. I was having chemotherapy at the time which made me very ill indeed. He said all his training was to make people better and yet I came in to hospital perfectly well and he made me ill. I was grateful to him. It made me feel more like a person and less like a patient.

The best definition I have found of what I want from my doctor in the way of emotional support comes from Carl Rogers' definition of a good psychotherapist. He defines three essential qualities of a "person centred approach". Firstly, genuineness or "no professional front or personal facade" on the part of the therapist; secondly acceptance or "unconditional positive regard" toward the client. His third quality is "empathic understand" of which he says: "This kind of sensitive active listening is exceedingly rare in our lives. We think we listen but very rarely do we listen with real understanding, true empathy. Yet listening, of this very special kind, is one of the most potent forces for change that I know." (2)

I am aware that I am describing the ideal cancer doctor as something of a paragon. And I've not finished yet. I also want my cancer doctor to encourage me to help myself. If taking responsibility for one's own health is important when a person is well, it is not going to become less so if they are ill.

What should the cancer doctor's role be in regard to complementary therapies? It should be more pro-active than simply permitting his patient to explore the minefield of what is available. I want more from my doctor than a pat on the head and a "of course dear, if you want to try one of those weird and wonderful therapies it is up to you."

When I was first diagnosed I discovered many books on the "Cure Yourself of Cancer" theme. Well meaning friends and relatives gave me many more. You name it there's a book by someone claiming it can cure cancer. It is only the methods that differ: rejecting orthodox medicine, meditating five times a day, living on nothing but beansprouts, indulging in herbal concoctions and coffee enemas, gazing at crystals, faith healing, etcetera. But mixed in with the fairly extreme I also found the so-called alternatives emphasised what seemed to be pretty much common sense: the importance of a positive attitude and what is more how it could be developed: relaxation -- self evident if you think about the trauma and uncertainty cancer patients have to live with; exercise and healthy eating. All this seemed to be full compatible with orthodox medicine but it wasn't something my doctors ever mentioned. The things which seemed so simple always seemed to be part of a general philosophy I couldn't believe and extreme remedies I couldn't face. I spent many hours agonizing whether or not it was worth trying anything if I couldn't swallow the whole package.

It takes a great deal of stamina and hard work to separate out the common sense from the fringe and the bogus science. Again I come back to the point I made earlier about how shocking a diagnosis of cancer is. For me it was difficult enough coping from day to day. I had very little energy and initiative left over. Yet I needed so much for exploring what I could do to help myself. I was deeply distressed for many months by the bewildering choices and contradictions. I am sure that other, sicker, patients simply give up the struggle.

I realise it would be unrealistic for cancer doctors to personally provide advice to all their patients on every aspect of self help. But I do expect him or her to provide some general encouragement, some recognition that these things are beneficial, and a controlled means of access to them. Doctors are not simply providers of care to their patients, they are managers of care. If they do not wish to get involved themselves, perhaps it would be appropriate to, for example, train a nurse to provide relaxation sessions, or invite other practitioners to provide sessions in areas where they have expertise. It might be difficult to begin with what I see as the ideal, where a wide variety of such therapies are available as part of a routine outpatient clinic. Nevertheless I think these would not be too difficult to introduce either into an inpatient ward or by means of a regular doctor-led support group.

I know many doctors are suspicious of complementary therapies because they are difficult to evaluate scientifically. Difficult but not impossible, as you have heard some of the previous speakers explain at this conference. But scientific evaluation misses the point. Many therapists claim not cure but healing, that they make patients feel better; and this is much harder to evaluate. Yet improving quality of life is as legitimate a medical objective as curing patients. It always has been. You are probably all familiar with that medieval French description of a doctor's role: "to cure sometimes, to relieve often, to comfort always". And to come up to date, WHO's strategy: "Health for all by the year 2000" reminds us that adding life to years is as important as adding years to life.

This is only one patient's list, and I have come up with quite a long one of what I want from my cancer doctor. The best clinical skills of course, and even better communication skills. I want him or her to set up sensitive systems of patient management which recognise my vulnerabilities, provide emotional care and encourage me to do what I can to help myself. I don't think my views are untypical but they are unique because every patient's experience is unique. If you want to know what YOUR patients want can I suggest that you ask them. You might learn a great deal from the answers.

Notes

(1) 'Getting it taped: the "bad news" consultation with cancer patients' by B. Hogbin and L. Fallowfield in British Journal of Hospital Medicine, Vol. 41, April 1989.

(2) A Way of Being, C.R. Rogers, Boston 1980, pp. 115-6.

ANNE DENNISON

....

In sickness and in health

Anne Dennison's death at the age of 37 has deprived the Department of Health of an able administrator and imaginative policy maker. She came to this country from New Zealand in 1976 with a scholarship to do historical research at Birkbeck College. Having gained a doctorate she joined the DHSS in 1980 and became a principal in 1987. She made a distinctive contribution in several areas, most notably in helping to change the way health and local authorities deal with communicable disease.

But she may be best remembered for the way in which she faced up to her diagnosis in 1985 of ovarian cancer. Characteristically, she used much of the time that remained to teach, write and speak about her experience as a patient. This led to journalism in this newspaper and the *British Medical Journal*, to the writing and editing of patient information booklets and the setting up of a patient support group at King's College Hospital.

She and her husband Paul faced her illness with courage, resolution and laughter. In the end, it became for her part of life itself and part of a process of discovery which continued until the end.

—————————————

Roy Cunningham

—————————————

Anne Dennison, born September 11 1954, died 17 July 1992.

reprinted with permission from *The Guardian*